EDITOR IN CHIEF: *Edie Soldinger*

MANAGING EDITOR: Stacy Abbate
RESTAURANT CORRESPONDENT: Maia Madden
ART & PRODUCTION DIRECTOR: Thomas Morgan
CONTRIBUTING WRITERS: Norman Roby, Richard DiMeola & Michael Frank
PHOTOGRAPHERS: Anthony Abuzeide & Greg Schneider

PUBLISHERS: **Cynthia & Richard Brault**

ADVERTISING DIRECTOR: Lee Nicole Weber
ADVERTISING MANAGER: Denise Valenza
RESTAURANT LIAISON: Michael Klein
ADVERTISING ASSOCIATE: Andrea Stargiotti
ASSISTANT TO THE PUBLISHER: Paula Mayer

CHAIRMAN OF THE BOARD: *Larry J. Soldinger*

DIRECTOR OF OPERATIONS: Susy Rein
ACCOUNTING MANAGER: Ben Soldinger
ADMINISTRATIVE ASSISTANT: Kim Wilson

THANKS TO

BAUME & MERCIER, CHRISTIAN DIOR, MERCEDES-BENZ, VACHERON CONSTANTIN AND FELISSIMO THIS COVER HELPS RAISE THOUSANDS OF DOLLARS FOR CHARITY.

Photographer: Uli Rose
Talent representative: Stockland Martel.
On location at: American Renaissance, NYC
Cover Design: Matt Foster

Epicurean Rendezvous is published by Baron Publishing Co., Inc.
3850 North Wilke Road, Suite 250, Arlington Heights, Illinois 60004
Tel: 708.259.1144 Fax: 708.259.8734 Copyright © 1995

ISBN 0-933875-31-2

History of Epicurean Rendezvous 5

Visa Card & VIP Membership Club 7

Restaurants

Northern California Map 13

San Francisco 15

Marin...79

East Bay...86

South Bay 97

Wine Country 111

Monterey/Carmel................................129

Yosemite...129

WORLD CLASS WINES

An expert recommends the best of the best

BY NORMAN ROBY 139

THE BEST OF CIGARS

Cigar Smoking Enjoys a Renaissance

BY RICHARD L. DI MEOLA 151

The Dominican Republic

BY MICHAEL FRANK.......................................161

Restaurant Index...168

SYMBOLS

ROMANTIC	🍴	☎		RESERVATIONS ACCEPTED
LIVELY	🙂	🍸		FULL BAR
JACKET AND TIE REQUIRED	🤵	🚗		VALET PARKING
LIVE ENTERTAINMENT	🎵	📷		VIEW

PURE STATEMENT.

SMIRNOFF.

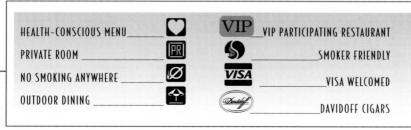

HEALTH-CONSCIOUS MENU _____ ♥	**VIP** ___VIP PARTICIPATING RESTAURANT
PRIVATE ROOM _____ PR	_____SMOKER FRIENDLY
NO SMOKING ANYWHERE _____ Ø	**VISA** _____VISA WELCOMED
OUTDOOR DINING _____	_____DAVIDOFF CIGARS

There are some restaurants where
the preference for the finer things
goes beyond just food and wine.

VISA

It's everywhere you want to be.

Epicurean Rendezvous is an annual guide to the best restaurants for those with discerning tastes. An award program, as well as a guide, Epicurean Rendezvous has five editions promoting the finest restaurants in New York, Chicago, Southern California, Northern California and Florida.

Only the best restaurants in each geographic area, as determined by an advisory board of food and wine experts, are invited to participate in the Epicurean Rendezvous Award Winning Program. As a member of this distinguished group, each awarded Epicurean Rendezvous restaurant has agreed to:

1. Dedicate itself to the support and promotion of fellow Epicurean Rendezvous restaurants in the continuing enhancement of fine dining.

2. Continue to strive towards perfection in their industry.

3. Participate in various philanthropic programs that will allow Epicurean Rendezvous and its partners to make donations to charitable organizations on behalf of its restaurants, advertisers and fine dining programs.

In order to receive the Epicurean Rendezvous Award For Excellence, an invited restaurant must ascribe to all of the above requirements. Sometimes a restaurant which has been selected by the advisory board declines to participate in all of the requirements which are necessary in order to become a member of this elite fraternity. For that reason those restaurants are not included in this guide.

The criteria for selection as an Epicurean Rendezvous restaurant are the following:

1. The restaurant must serve consistently outstanding cuisine.

2. The staff must be courteous and knowledgeable and provide consistently excellent service.

3. The decor must be attractive and the ambiance congenial.

4. The wine list must have the breadth and balance to complement the cuisine.

Every year both new contenders and previous award-winners are re-evaluated. The publishers personally screen the finalists and the ultimate determinations are made. Sometimes a restaurant will not meet every criterion but is so strong in one area that it deserves an award.

Once the award winning restaurants are chosen, Epicurean Rendezvous leaves all critique behind. The only goal is to promote and elevate those who work hard to maintain the standards of fine dining. Sold on newsstands and in bookstores, the guides are also available in the restaurants, thereby creating a nationwide network of Epicurean Rendezvous diners.

Think of our reviews as short guided tours of each restaurant. They put you inside the dining room and introduce you to the owner or manager. You meet the chef, learn a little about his or her cooking style, and look over a sample menu. By the time you call for reservations, you'll feel confident that you've made the right choice.

INTRODUCING

GODET

Delicious Belgian White Chocolate Liqueur Blended with Aged Cognac.

Godet is the combination of the finest milled Belgian white chocolate with mellow aged cognac for a luscious, indulgent taste cherished the world over. Fortunately, this incredible taste is now available in the United States.

GODET

ESTABLISHED 1838

The Epicurean Rendezvous

VISA CARD & VIP MEMBERSHIP CLUB

To be an Epicurean Rendezvous Visa VIP Club Member is to be included in a very special group of people who seek out, rejoice in, and respect unique and memorable dining experiences. As an Epicurean Rendezvous Visa card holder, you can expect various kinds of special and individual treatment, from the time you first identify yourself on the telephone to the last personal good-bye you receive at the door.

At our participating restaurants designated by this symbol **VIP**, you will receive very personal attention throughout the meal from the chef, owner, maitre d' or manager, and at many of these restaurants you will be given preferred seating and guaranteed on-time reservations. Our award winning chefs and managers will want to share a complimentary tasting with you, perhaps a newly created appetizer course, a specially selected pasta course, a unique dessert course or sampling, or perhaps a particular complimentary glass of champagne or wine that best enhances your meal. Because every restaurant is different and every customer is different, the VIP recognition will vary greatly.

Epicurean Rendezvous restaurants share in an uncompromising commitment to the evolution and the ever improving quality of the overall dining experience. They epitomize the creative bond between chefs and restaurants, their continuing endeavors in striving for excellence, and in their wish to share their individual talents with those special diners who most appreciate them.

Obviously some experiences will be better than others. But by being an Epicurean Rendezvous Visa card holder you can be assured of the most notable evening that a particular restaurant is capable of offering.

Whether you try a new restaurant around the corner from your home or whether you are traveling across the nation, you now have the ability to look up the restaurant of your choice, see what the dining room looks like, see who the owners and chefs are, learn about the history, style, menus, location, times of operation and now even the ultimate – you will be treated like a very special friend from the moment you walk in the door.

*Apply for your Epicurean
Rendezvous Visa Card today.*

Myth – [*all vodkas are the same.*]
We pass every ounce over a bed of pure *Quartz* crystals, not once, but twice.
And in between these steps it is filtered through virgin granules of activated carbon
made from the wood of Russia's *Native Birch* tree. Thus a spirit is born so *Refined*
that some have called *Stolichnaya* CRISTALL...*flawless*™.

Ever wonder why she's holding a light?
For a great smoke, take a few liberties.

 Finally, a welcome sign for both smokers and nonsmokers.
Call 1-800-494-5444 for more information.

15 mg "tar," 1.1 mg nicotine av. per cigarette by FTC method.

SURGEON GENERAL'S WARNING: Cigarette
Smoke Contains Carbon Monoxide.

BENSON & HEDGES 100's

THE LENGTH YOU GO TO FOR PLEASURE

home

fashion

garden

Exclusive FELISSIMO 56
earl grey tea fragrance
collection. $30-80

HIDALGO RINGS in 18k
gold and enamel.
$290-635
18k gold and diamond
bands. $185-760

Photography by Ann Stratton and Daniel Aubry for Felissimo

artspace

tearoom

FELISSIMO

10 west 56th street NYC

mon-sat 10-6 thurs 10-8 212.247.5656
visit our tearoom for lunch or afternoon haiku tea
corporate gift, personal shopping,
bridal registry 212.247.7474
to request our catalog 800.708.7690

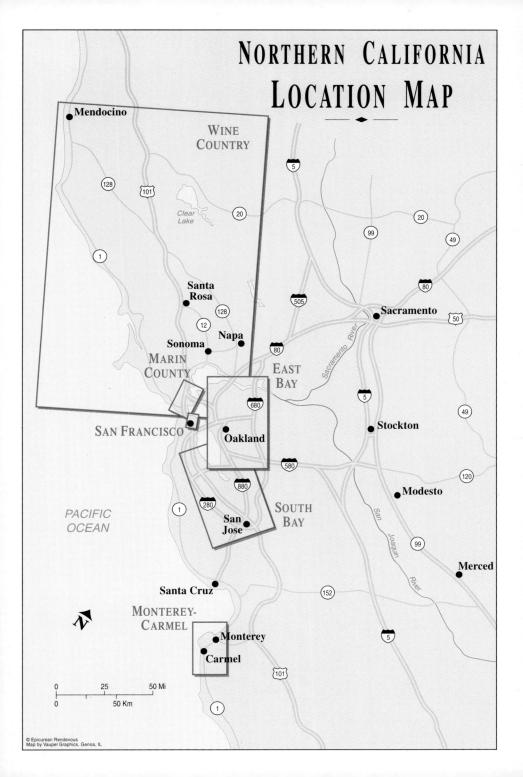

NORTHERN CALIFORNIA
LOCATION MAP

Mendocino

WINE
COUNTRY

⑤ 5

128 101

Clear
Lake

⑳ 20

⑳ 20

⑨ 99

㊾ 49

Santa
Rosa

128

⑤ 505

Sacramento

㊿ 50

1

12

Napa

Sonoma

⑧ 80

MARIN
COUNTY

EAST
BAY

Sacramento River

⑤ 5

㊾ 49

SAN FRANCISCO

⑥ 680

Oakland

Stockton

⑤ 580

PACIFIC
OCEAN

1

⑧ 880

② 280

San
Jose

SOUTH
BAY

San

⑫ 120

Modesto

⑨ 99

Merced

Santa Cruz

Joaquin

MONTEREY-
CARMEL

⑮ 152

River

N

Monterey

⑤ 5

Carmel

| 0 | 25 | 50 Mi |
| 0 | | 50 Km |

101

① 1

© Epicurean Rendevous
Map by Vaupel Graphics, Genoa, IL

IT'S NOT TRESPASSING WHEN YOU CROSS YOUR OWN BOUNDARIES.

Imported Blended Scotch Whisky, 40% Alc./Vol. (80°)
©1995 Schieffelin & Somerset Co., New York, N.Y.

Johnnie Walker
BLACK LABEL
AGED 12 YEARS

THERE'S MORE TO EXPLORE IN BLACK.

The resonating taste whispers beyond the expected.

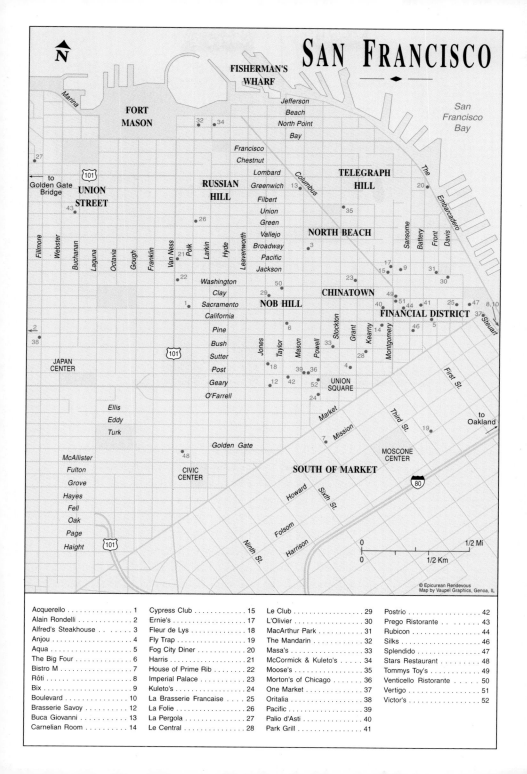

SAN FRANCISCO

N

FISHERMAN'S WHARF

FORT MASON

RUSSIAN HILL

TELEGRAPH HILL

NORTH BEACH

CHINATOWN

NOB HILL

FINANCIAL DISTRICT

UNION STREET

to Golden Gate Bridge

JAPAN CENTER

CIVIC CENTER

UNION SQUARE

SOUTH OF MARKET

MOSCONE CENTER

to Oakland

San Francisco Bay

The Embarcadero

© Epicurean Rendevous
Map by Vaupel Graphics, Genoa, IL

0   1/2 Mi
0   1/2 Km

Streets / labels: Marina, Jefferson, Beach, North Point, Bay, Francisco, Chestnut, Lombard, Greenwich, Filbert, Union, Green, Vallejo, Broadway, Pacific, Jackson, Washington, Clay, Sacramento, California, Pine, Bush, Sutter, Post, Geary, O'Farrell, Ellis, Eddy, Turk, Golden Gate, McAllister, Fulton, Grove, Hayes, Fell, Oak, Page, Haight, Fillmore, Webster, Buchanan, Laguna, Octavia, Gough, Franklin, Van Ness, Polk, Larkin, Hyde, Leavenworth, Jones, Taylor, Mason, Powell, Stockton, Grant, Kearny, Montgomery, Columbus, Sansome, Battery, Front, Davis, Steuart, First St., Third St., Market, Mission, Howard, Sixth St., Folsom, Ninth St., Harrison

Acquerello 1	Cypress Club 15	Le Club 29	Postrio 42
Alain Rondelli 2	Ernie's 17	L'Olivier 30	Prego Ristorante 43
Alfred's Steakhouse 3	Fleur de Lys 18	MacArthur Park 31	Rubicon 44
Anjou 4	Fly Trap 19	The Mandarin 32	Silks 46
Aqua 5	Fog City Diner 20	Masa's 33	Splendido 47
The Big Four 6	Harris 21	McCormick & Kuleto's 34	Stars Restaurant 48
Bistro M 7	House of Prime Rib 22	Moose's 35	Tommys Toy's 49
Rôti 8	Imperial Palace 23	Morton's of Chicago 36	Venticello Ristorante 50
Bix 9	Kuleto's 24	One Market 37	Vertigo 51
Boulevard 10	La Brasserie Francaise 25	Oritalia 38	Victor's 52
Brasserie Savoy 12	La Folie 26	Pacific 39	
Buca Giovanni 13	La Pergola 27	Palio d'Asti 40	
Carnelian Room 14	Le Central 28	Park Grill 41	

AQUA

252 CALIFORNIA STREET
BETWEEN FRONT & BATTERY
SAN FRANCISCO, CA 94111
(415) 956-9662

Visa & Major Credit Cards
Dinner Mon-Sat • Lunch Mon-Fri

Proprietor
CHARLES T. CONDY

Chef/Proprietor
MICHAEL MINA

Recommended Items

Appetizers

BLACK MUSSEL SOUFFLÉ WITH
CHARDONNAY, GARLIC &
PARSLEY • GRILLED MAINE
LOBSTER SALAD WITH SONOMA
TOMATOES, BASIL OIL

Entrées

ATLANTIC COD STEAK
WITH HORSERADISH MASHED
POTATOES, MUSTARD SAUCES
• MAINE BROOK TROUT WITH
POTATO CRUST, HERB-BRAISED
CHANTERELLES, FENNEL JUS
• MEDALLIONS OF RARE AHI,
SEARED HUDSON VALLEY FOIE
GRAS, PINOT NOIR SAUCE

DESCRIBED BY OWNERS GEORGE AND STACEY MORRONE AS A specialty seafood restaurant, Aqua is dedicated exclusively to fish. New Jersey-born George Morrone believes that "the best restaurants devote their attention to the kitchen." As chef, he creates dishes that are true to the integrity of the fish, letting the natural juices and flavors speak for themselves, enhancing selections with delicate herbs, light sauces and essences of vegetables only. ◆ The light and flower-filled dining room echoes the kitchen's emphasis on understatement. Two large, metal-framed mirrors tilt away from the walls, a rich mix of plaster and paint, both capturing a room full of lively diners. Like the menu, and a reflection of the Morrone's endless attention to detail, the slipcovers on the chairs change with the seasons. ◆ To the left of the entrance, oil and gesso paint landscapes by Wade Hoefer celebrate California's beauty, while on the right, a friendly bar invites guests to linger over a Champagne cocktail and watch the cablecars go by.

AVERAGE DINNER FOR TWO: $85
DOES NOT INCLUDE WINE, TAX AND GRATUITY

ACQUERELLO

1722 SACRAMENTO STREET
NEAR VAN NESS & POLK
SAN FRANCISCO, CA 94109
(415) 567-5432

Visa & Major Credit Cards
Closed Sunday & Monday • Dinner Only

Proprietor
GIANCARLO PATERLINI

Chef/Proprietor
SUZETTE GRESHAM

Recommended Items
♦♕♦

Appetizers
CARPACCIO OF BEEF WITH
SMOKED SALMON SAUCE
• RIDGED PASTA DELICATELY
SCENTED WITH FOIE GRAS &
BLACK TRUFFLE

Entrées
WILD BOAR SAUSAGE WITH
NATURAL GLAZE OVER GREENS
• LOIN OF LAMB WRAPPED IN
PANCETTA WITH GARLIC,
PARSLEY & RED WINE •
MARINATED FILET OF HALIBUT
WITH CARAMELIZED SHALLOTS,
TOMATOES & THYME

ACQUERELLO MEANS WATERCOLOR IN ITALIAN, AND ENTERING the restaurant's dining room is like stepping into a painting. Pale pink walls dotted with soft lamps, a changing watercolor exhibit and pastel bouquets blend light and color, while clay tiles and rural beams provide contrast. ♦ Hailed as one of San Francisco's best Italian chefs when she was at Donatello, Suzette Gresham has a talent for rustic-style cooking, and her seasonal menu spans all regions of Italy. Proprietor Giancarlo Paterlini, a Bologna native who has earned a fine reputation in the restaurant business over the last nineteen years, met Gresham when he was the manager of Donatello. ♦ Uncovering lesser-known, interesting Italian and California vintages is Paterlini's passion, and offering them at a reasonable price is his forte. Once a month, Acquerello presents a special regional menu paired with the wines of a particular vintner, a rare opportunity to sample the talents of this inspired partnership.

AVERAGE DINNER FOR TWO: $70
DOES NOT INCLUDE WINE, TAX AND GRATUITY

ALAIN RONDELLI

126 CLEMENT STREET
SAN FRANCISCO, CA 94118
(415) 387-0408

Visa & MasterCard Only
Dinner Tues–Sun

General Manager
JEAN-LUC HITTA

Chef/Proprietor
ALAIN RONDELLI

Recommended Items

Appetizers
PEAR & ROQUEFORT WITH
CHAMPAGNE, VINEGAR & BLACK
PEPPER GASTRIQUE • FOIE GRAS
& FIGS, WARM BRIOCHE
• CRAB WITH TOMATO WATER
& ASPARAGUS

Entrées
LAMB EN POT-AU-FEU WITH
HORSERADISH & LEMON
VINAIGRETTE
• LOBSTER, FAVA BEANS IN
ORANGE & ANIS BROTH,
PAPRIKA CRISP
• TRIPE PROVENÇAL,
V.G.E. STYLE

NO STRANGER TO TERRIFIC PRESS, *GOURMET* RECENTLY ADDED another feather to Alain Rondelli's toque with the assertion, "This is better than Paris at three times *less* the price." They were referring to Rondelli's new restaurant, opened only one year ago yet already a food lover's destination. Says the chef, "I want to bring San Francisco the French food of today, a taste of what's happening in France right now." ♦ A consummate artist in the kitchen, Rondelli explores new levels of excitement with tireless drive. He is passionate about his work to the point of obsession. "I am constantly, endlessly making improvements for my customers," states the chef. One such improvement is the newly remodeled dining room. Small (17 tables) and elegant, it allows his expert team to lavish special attention on each and every diner. The menu and wine list are also condensed and select, just right for the restaurant's sophisticated, well-traveled patrons.

AVERAGE DINNER FOR TWO: $70
DOES NOT INCLUDE WINE, TAX AND GRATUITY

ALFRED'S STEAKHOUSE

886 BROADWAY
AT BROADWAY TUNNEL
SAN FRANCISCO, CA 94133
(415) 781-7058

Visa & Major Credit Cards
Open Daily for Dinner • Lunch Thursday Only

Proprietor
ART PETRI

Proprietor
AL PETRI

Recommended Items

Appetizers
ESCARGOTS BOURGUIGNONNE
• ITALIAN FRIED
CALAMARI • FRESH OYSTERS
ON THE HALF SHELL • CAESAR
SALAD • FRESH ARTICHOKE

Entrées
ALFRED'S BONE-IN NEW YORK
STEAK • CHATEAUBRIAND OF
BEEF TENDERLOIN, SAUCE
BÉARNAISE, CARVED AT THE
TABLE • FILET MIGNON OF BEEF
TENDERLOIN • FRESH SALMON,
MESQUITE-BROILED

SINCE 1928, ALFRED'S HAS SERVED ONLY THE FINEST PRIME CUTS of juicy corn-fed, skillfully aged steaks broiled over imported Mexican mesquite charcoal, producing tender, distinctively flavorful meat. Owner Al Petri recommends a tangy Caesar salad and an order of tortellini in a creamy pesto sauce as a start to dinner. ♦ At Alfred's, customers deliberate whether to order beef, veal, chicken or seafood and whether to have it mesquite-grilled or prepared in traditional Italian style. The cannelloni and fettuccine in particular, are evidence of the North Beach-Italian tradition maintained at Alfred's. ♦ A thoroughly professional staff provides personal, attentive service in a rich clublike atmosphere that exudes Victorian luxury. Upstairs, banquet rooms can handle private parties of fifteen to fifty. Alfred's, offering the best of meat-and-potatoes Americana with an Italian touch, is an enduring San Francisco institution.

AVERAGE DINNER FOR TWO: $70
DOES NOT INCLUDE WINE, TAX AND GRATUITY

ANJOU

44 CAMPTON PLACE
AT UNION SQUARE
SAN FRANCISCO, CA 94108
(415) 392-5373
Visa & Major Credit Cards
Lunch & Dinner Tues-Sat

Proprietor
GAIL MORIN

Chef/Proprietor
PIERRE MORIN

Recommended Items

Appetizers
ASPARAGUS WITH AN ESSENCE
OF MORELS • RILLETTE OF
SMOKED SALMON, SALAD OF
TENDER LIMA BEANS, THYME
& SUNDRIED TOMATOS

Entrées
GRILLED MARINATED WILD
STURGEON, WHITE FRISÉE SALAD
& POTATO SCALLION ROLL
•SMOKED CHICKEN, SAUTÉED
WILD MUSHROOMS, MIXED HERB
POLENTA, & SEASONAL MIXED
GREENS • CHILEAN SEA BASS
MARINATED IN WHOLE GRAIN
MUSTARD, SERVED BROILED

A STYLISH FRENCH BISTRO, ANJOU IS A FAVORITE DOWNTOWN rendezvous by day and an upbeat dinner house by night, close to business, shopping and the theatre. The new name is inspired by the region near the Loire Valley also known as "The Garden of France," a place where Pierre Morin's family lived for generations. ♦ The chef's menu reflects the seasons, fusing bistro favorites and innovative signature dishes based on traditional French cuisine. Lunch and dinner menus are identical, with the exception of a daily special entrée which is only available at dinner. There is a daily "express" menu, like the traditional "plat du jour" as well as a daily seafood special. All desserts are housemade. ♦ *Gourmet* calls Anjou "one of San Francisco's most satisfying French bistros." *"Esquire* and *The New York Times* raved about Janot's, and we plan to do even better as Anjou,"says Morin. He's off to a good start: Anjou was recently voted one of the region's "Top 100" by *Condé Nast Traveler* readers.

AVERAGE DINNER FOR TWO: $50
DOES NOT INCLUDE WINE, TAX AND GRATUITY

IT WAS DESIGNED TO
PROTECT HEADS OF STATE.
NOT TO MENTION ARMS, LEGS
AND FEET OF STATE.

Mercedes-Benz of North America, Inc.

THE BOMBAY SAPPHIRE MARTINI. AS ARRANGED BY ULLA DARNI.

P O U R   S O M E T H I N G   P R I C E L E S S.

Bombay® Sapphire™ Gin. 47% alc/vol (94 Proof). 100% neutral spirits. ©1994 Carillon Importers, LTD., Teaneck, N.J. ©1994 Ulla Darni.

BISTRO M

HOTEL MILANO

55 FIFTH STREET
SAN FRANCISCO, CA 94103
(415) 543-5554

Visa & Major Credit Cards
Open Daily • Breakfast, Lunch & Dinner

Manager
FRANCIS J LEBAILLIF

Chef de Cuisine
ANTHONY PELS, JR.

Recommended Items

Appetizers
ONION TART • SAUTÉED
FOIE GRAS WITH FRESH
CORN POLENTA • SMOKED
SALMON TERRINE WITH APPLE
& CHAYOTE MEDLEY

Entrées
SCALLOPS NAPOLEON WITH
SAFFRON SAUCE • DUCK
CONFIT WITH BRAISED
ENDIVES • LAMB SHANK
MOROCCAN STYLE

AFTER WOOING DINERS IN LOS ANGELES, SANTA BARBARA, Washington, D.C., Baltimore and Philadelphia, Michel Richard set out to seduce San Francisco. His mission was victorious. Resident foodies soon had to admit his Bistro M was a winner. Located next door to the San Francisco Centre, it has beautiful high ceilings, a row of two-story arched windows and a stunning wrap-around mural by artist Wayne R. Olds depicting an abstract panorama of city scenes. ♦ And the food? It's hard to resist Michel's singular combination of crunchy and soft textures, rich yet simple flavors. Executed by Chef Anthony Pels, Jr., the menu features Richard's signature dishes, from a stellar onion tart to the best *gratin Dauphinois* in town. Like any top restaurant in France, Bistro M presents an outstanding selection of cheeses, but don't skip the desserts. Richard started his career as a pastry chef, and it shows. One bite of the hot chocolate cake, oozing pure chocolate, transports diners to heaven. ♦ Casual, lively, and staffed by a friendly, savvy crew, Bistro M is a bright star in San Francisco's restaurant constellation.

AVERAGE DINNER FOR TWO: $65
DOES NOT INCLUDE WINE, TAX AND GRATUITY

The Big Four

HUNTINGTON HOTEL
1075 California Street
San Francisco, Ca 94108
(415) 771-1140

Visa & Major Credit Cards
Open Daily • Breakfast, Lunch & Dinner

Manager
Newton A. Cope, Jr.

Chef
Gloria
Ciccarone-Nehls

Recommended Items

Appetizers

Venison Chili, Black Beans
Cheddar & Onion Crisps
• Pan-Fried Dungeness Crab
Cakes over Field Greens,
Creamy Caper Vinaigrette

Entrées

Rack of Lamb , Mustard-Herb
Crust & Orange-Onion
Marmalade in a Cracked
Pepper-Zinfandel Sauce
• Fettuccine, Prosciutto,
Fried Sage, Wild Mushrooms,
Thyme & Cream • Pan
Roasted Salmon, Almond-
Citrus Crust & Crispy
Artichoke & Saffron Glaze

NAMED FOR SAN FRANCISCO'S "BIG FOUR" – RAILROAD TYCOONS C.P. Huntington, Charles Crocker, Mark Hopkins and Leland Stanford—the restaurant showcases owner Newton Cope Sr.'s collection of California art, Big Four political cartoons, railroad prints and other historical memorabilia. ♦ Popular for power lunches, the Big Four shifts in the evening towards a romantic ambiance, with live piano music and the warmth of a fireplace, elements that keep its reputation as a timeless tradition atop Nob Hill going strong. ♦ For more than sixteen years, Executive Chef Gloria Ciccarone-Nehls has created menus that are definitely contemporary yet reflective of her extensive classical training. "We are receptive to innovation, especially with our daily specials," she says, "but we pride ourselves on serving local ingredients and a menu that changes with the seasons." The chef has also recently added a number of lighter menu selections to her repertoire.

AVERAGE DINNER FOR TWO: $60
DOES NOT INCLUDE WINE, TAX AND GRATUITY

AMERICAN

BIX

56 GOLD STREET
AT MONTGOMERY
SAN FRANCISCO, CA 94133
(415) 433-6300

Visa & Major Credit Cards
Open Daily for Dinner • Lunch Mon-Fri

Proprietor
DOUG BIEDERBECK

Executive Chef
DANIEL D. DELONG

Recommended Items

♣

Appetizers
WALDORF SALAD
WITH ROQUEFORT &
WALNUTS • STEAK
TARTARE • CRISP POTATO
& LEEK PANCAKE
WITH SMOKED
SALMON & CAVIAR

Entrées
CHICKEN HASH A LA BIX
•GRILLED FILET MIGNON WITH
POMMES FRITES & BEARNAISE
• GRILLED PORK CHOP
WITH MASHED POTATOES,
ROASTED SHALLOTS & SOUR
CHERRIES

TO REACH ONE OF SAN FRANCISCO'S LIVELIEST RESTAURANTS, go down a quiet alley off Montgomery Street near Jackson Square to a plain brick building flanked by antique galleries. Inside is Bix, a tribute to the Jazz Age and Art Moderne that Doug ("Bix") Biederbeck calls "an updated supper club," complete with torch singer, saxophone player and pianist. ♦ Bix recalls the era of the majestic ocean liner, with curving Honduras mahogany, silver columns and reproductions of late 1920s ceiling lamps. A huge, deep-hued mural of a jazz club scene is the focal point. Underneath, behind the always-jammed bar, white-jacketed bartenders revel in the renaissance of the cocktail with deftly prepared Manhattans, Sidecars and Martinis. ♦ The menu is filled with offerings that sound simple and straightforward. Modern culinary flourishes jazz up each one, to surprise and delight the palate.

AVERAGE DINNER FOR TWO: $60
DOES NOT INCLUDE WINE, TAX AND GRATUITY

BOULEVARD

ONE MISSION
AT STEUART
SAN FRANCISCO, CA 94105
(415) 543-6084

Visa & Major Credit Cards
Open Daily for Dinner • Lunch Mon-Fri

Designer/Proprietor
PAT KULETO

Chef/Proprietor
NANCY OAKES

Recommended Items

Appetizers

ROASTED BUTTERNUT
SQUASH SOUP, SHIITAKES
STUFFED WITH GOAT CHEESE

• SAUTÉED ZUCCHINI BLOSSOMS,
LEMON THYME GNOCCHI,
MORELS, FAVA BEAN
& SAFFRON SAUCE

Entrées

PAN-ROASTED SALMON ON A
BED OF SWEET WHITE CORN,
MORELS & GRILLED ASPARAGUS,
THYME VERMOUTH SAUCE

• MAPLE-CURED PORK LOIN
SPIT ROASTED, POTATO
FRITTERS, ASSORTED
VEGETABLES

A SENSATIONAL EVOLUTION FROM L'AVENUE WHERE NANCY Oakes made her name, Boulevard is also a personal fantasy of Pat Kuleto, the man who changed the meaning of restaurant design in California. Together they give Boulevard a level of comfort and versatility that put you at ease whether you walk through the revolving front door wearing blue jeans or Armani. ♦ New England roots made Oakes a believer in American food early on. Although her dishes, like the designs of Kuleto, appear intricate, they are really quite accessible. Each course, including some amazing desserts, carries a depth of flavor that can aptly be called soulful. ♦ The narrow 1889 building, that houses the 130-seat restaurant adds character to the space that is decorated with recurring images of peacocks. The dining room is divided into three distinct sections characterized by a swirling brick ceiling, street lamps and innumerable small tiles and light fixtures. Windows in the back overlook the Ferry Building and Bay Bridge.

AVERAGE DINNER FOR TWO: $60
DOES NOT INCLUDE WINE, TAX AND GRATUITY

Christian Dior

Nordstrom

For more information or to place an order, please call Christian Dior: 1-800-929-3000

Guess who's behind
this great tasting non-alcoholic brew.

Good guess. The brewers of Heineken have created Buckler. It's the rich, refreshing non-alcoholic brew that has all the character of a fine import. In fact, just one sip and you'll realize the obvious…nobody *but* Heineken could have come up with something so good.

Buckler. The only thing that's closer to beer…is beer.

BRASSERIE SAVOY

580 GEARY STREET
AT JONES
SAN FRANCISCO, CA 94102
(415) 471-2700

Visa & Major Credit Cards
Open Daily • Breakfast & Dinner

Restaurant Manager
TERRY GREENSTREET

Executive Chef
DEAN JAMES MAX

Recommended Items

Appetizers

SELECTION OF PACIFIC
OYSTERS • SALAD OF
SMOKED DUCK BREAST, BABY
GREENS, WALNUT VINAIGRETTE
• BEEF CARPACCIO

Entrées

GRILLED SALMON ON A BED
OF ISRAELI COUSCOUS
• ROASTED LAMB CHOPS
WITH NAPOLEON OF POTATO
PURÉE, SAUTÉED SPINACH, RED
CABBAGE & GARLIC SAUCE

TAKE A TYPICAL PARISIAN BRASSERIE, FILTER IT THROUGH A generous dose of San Francisco tradition and the result is Brasserie Savoy, an elegant but friendly brasserie that adjoins the Royalton Savoy Hotel. Located in the theater district, Brasserie Savoy features fair prices and top caliber food in a vivacious and classy atmosphere. A collage of deeply polished cherry, maple and red birch set off by gleaming brass, black-and-white marble floor and a zinc-topped bar sets the brasserie mood. A knowledgeable and responsive wait staff enhances the cuisine. ♦ Executive Chef Dean Max emphasizes natural flavors and speaks to his clientele through his food. He does so brilliantly, with sumptuous risotto, roasted free range chicken, and other selections that make Brasserie Savoy a favorite, especially for pre-theater dining.

AVERAGE DINNER FOR TWO: $45
DOES NOT INCLUDE WINE, TAX AND GRATUITY

VIP

BUCA GIOVANNI

800 GREENWICH STREET
NEAR COLUMBUS
SAN FRANCISCO, CA 94133
(415) 776-7766
Visa & Major Credit Cards
Closed Sunday & Monday • Dinner Only

Proprietor
MICHELLE LEONI

Chef/Proprietor
GIOVANNI LEONI

Recommended Items

Appetizers
PANZEROTTI STUFFED WITH
ONIONS FROM BUCA
GIOVANNI'S RANCH
• ANTIPASTO MISTO LA BUCA
• ROUND RAVIOLINI STUFFED
WITH EGGPLANT &
GORGONZOLA IN A BASIL SAUCE

Entrées
RABBIT WITH GRAPPA
• VENISON WITH WILD FENNEL
• SCAMPI WITH FRESH
BABY ARTICHOKES • LAMB
STUFFED WITH MORTADELLA,
HERBS & PORCINI, WRAPPED
IN GRAPE LEAVES

TRUE TO ITS NAME, GIOVANNI'S "CAVE" IS A ROMANTIC BRICK-walled retreat down a short flight of stairs. The real action, however, is in the open kitchen upstairs, where those seated at the few small tables can watch Giovanni Leoni prepare his Tuscan specialties. ♦ Giovanni Leoni, who has been cooking in San Francisco for forty years, directs every aspect of Buca Giovanni. Up at dawn, he does the daily marketing, and on Sundays, returns from a visit to his family ranch in Ukiah with dozens of rabbits in the back of his car. Giovanni grows his own herbs, lettuce and tomatoes, and will search for years to find the best ricotta and the finest coffee beans, which he then roasts on the premises. ♦ His exacting standards can be tasted in every preparation, from the earthy *salsa rosa,* an addictive purée of sundried tomatoes, anchovies, garlic, capers and vinegar, to the ethereal eggplant cappelletti.

AVERAGE DINNER FOR TWO: $50
DOES NOT INCLUDE WINE, TAX AND GRATUITY

CARNELIAN ROOM

BANK OF AMERICA BUILDING
555 CALIFORNIA STREET
SAN FRANCISCO, CA 94104
(415) 433-7500

Visa & Major Credit Cards
Open Daily for Dinner • Sunday Brunch

General Manager	Chef
RALPH BÜRGIN	DWAYNE GRIFFITHS

Recommended items

Appetizers
SEARED VENISON
CARPACCIO • ESCARGOT
& WILD MUSHROOM RAGOUT

Entrées
AHI TUNA WITH GREEN
ONION CONFIT • DAY
BOAT SCALLOPS WITH
BLACK MUSSEL VINAIGRETTE
• ANGUS BEEF

SOARING FIFTY-TWO STORIES ABOVE SAN FRANCISCO'S FINANCIAL District, the Carnelian Room offers a panoramic view of the Bay Area. The Bank of America's polished granite building is a fitting home for this elegant dining establishment. ♦ Chef Dwayne Griffiths emphasizes seafood with his bounty of tempting selections along with California's rich variety of fresh seasonal produce and game. ♦ By day, the Carnelian Room is the exclusive Banker's Club, accessible only to members or by invitation. The restaurant is open to the public at night, for Sunday brunch and banquets and catered events. ♦ The Carnelian Room's extensive wine list is recipient of *The Wine Spectator* Grand Award and features a cellar of 36,000 bottles.

AVERAGE DINNER FOR TWO: $50
DOES NOT INCLUDE WINE, TAX AND GRATUITY

CYPRESS CLUB

500 JACKSON STREET
AT MONTGOMERY
SAN FRANCISCO, CA 94133
(415) 296-8555

Visa & Major Credit Cards
Open Daily for Dinner • Sunday Brunch

Proprietors
JOHN & RENÉE CUNIN

Chef
BENJAMIN DAVIS

Recommended Items

Appetizers

QUAIL WITH PRESERVED GINGER, BACON & WATER CHESTNUTS • POTATO & GARLIC RAVIOLI WITH DUCK CONFIT & SOUR CHERRIES • SCALLOPS WITH SWEET PEA RISOTTO & DAUBE OF MUSHROOMS

Entrées

BABY LAMB WITH MUSTARD GARLIC SPATZLE & MINT OIL • PEPPERED TUNA WITH BARLEY, WILD MUSHROOMS CELERY WATER

NO ONE COULD ACCUSE JOHN CUNIN AND NEWVISION RES-taurant Partners of not taking chances. Cypress Club is the successful fruit of their ambitious attempt to conjure a 1940s supper club, creating a stimulating environment for a one-of-a-kind dining experience. ♦ Every inch of the place is curvy and organic. Rounded partitions encased in copper, winding paths of mosaic tile and sensual archways bask in the restaurant's soft light. A colorful mural depicting Northern California surrounds the effervescent dining room supported by voluptuous columns, and nipple-like ceiling fixtures captivate patrons entering near the·bar, three-deep by 10 p.m. ♦ Born in London and reared in New Mexico, Chef Benjamin Davis likes to push creative boundaries with stunning dishes that are architectural wonders in keeping with the restaurant's spirit. Benjamin, like his predecessor Cory Schreiber, is devoted to locally grown food, mixing flavors and textures, and to creating exotic sauces.

AVERAGE DINNER FOR TWO: $70
DOES NOT INCLUDE WINE, TAX AND GRATUITY

ERNIE'S

847 MONTGOMERY STREET
AT PACIFIC
SAN FRANCISCO, CA 94133
(415) 397-5969

Visa & Major Credit Cards
Dinner Mon–Sat

Proprietors
VICTOR GOTTI
ROLAND GOTTI
General Manager
TERRY FISCHER

Chef
DAVID KINCH

Recommended Items

Appetizers
CHILLED DUNGENESS
CRAB & AVOCADO CAKE
WITH TOMATO GELÉE
• CLASSIC VICHYSSOISE WITH
OYSTERS WRAPPED IN LETTUCE
LEAVES WITH FRESH HERBS &
RYE TOASTS WITH GOAT CHEESE

Entrées
• GRILLED SALMON
"LACQUERED" WITH SWEET
MUSTARD, RAGOUT OF FENNEL
& LEEK PERFUMED WITH BASIL
• ROASTED RACK OF LAMB
WITH SPRING VEGETABLES &
NATURAL JUICES, BASIL OIL &
FAVA BEANS

IN A CITY OF RESTAURANT LEGENDS, ERNIE'S REIGNS SUPREME. What began in 1934 as a small Italian eatery with linoleum floors and modestly set tables has grown into a showplace of elegant decor and contemporary French cuisine using the freshest California ingredients. ♦ Renowned for his expertise in the kitchens of the four star Quilted Giraffe in New York and Silks at the Mandarin Oriental in San Francisco, gifted Chef David Kinch explains, "French and Asian techniques combined with American produce give me a completely different way of thinking about food." The mix enables him to maximize flavors while bringing an elegant simplicity to his presentations. ♦ The Bacchus Wine Cellar, available for private parties, houses a wine selection recognized as one of America's finest and honored by The Wine Spectator Grand Award since its inception. Ernie's was also a recipient of Mobil's Five Star Award for twenty-nine consecutive years — an American record.

AVERAGE DINNER FOR TWO: $90
DOES NOT INCLUDE WINE, TAX AND GRATUITY

33

VIP

FRENCH

FLEUR DE LYS

777 SUTTER STREET
NEAR JONES
SAN FRANCISCO, CA 94109
(415) 673-7779

Visa & Major Credit Cards
Closed Sunday • Dinner Only

Proprietor
MAURICE ROUAS

Chef/Proprietor
HUBERT KELLER

Recommended Items

Appetizers
SEA URCHIN MOUSSELINE,
PRESENTED ON SEA SCALLOP
WITH ASPARAGUS SAUCE
• NEW YORK STATE FOIE GRAS
TERRINE IN A BLACK PEPPER
& FRESH HERB GELÉE

Entrées
SEARED AHI TUNA
ON LIGHTLY CREAMED
SPINACH, SESAME
OIL VINAIGRETTE
• MARINATED LOIN OF
VENISON GLAZED WITH
MUSTARD SEED SABAYON,
SAUCE POIVRADE

EVEN THOUGH FLEUR DE LYS HAS HAD A DEVOTED CLIENTELE since it opened in 1970, in 1986 Maurice Rouas decided to give his restaurant a shot in the arm. He did what many others before him had tried without success: he lured the talented Hubert Keller to Fleur de Lys as his new partner and chef. ♦ Educated at the Hotel School in Strasbourg, France, Keller trained under such legendary chefs as Paul Haeberlin, Paul Bocuse, Gaston Lenôtre and Roger Vergé. "I believe," he says, "in the sweetness of the onion, the green of the striped tigerella, the subtlety of the leek, the pervasiveness of the garlic and the intensity of Florence fennel." In addition to Keller's regular menu, special vegetarian dishes such as Maryland crabcakes with creoja sauce are also available. ♦ The dramatic setting of Fleur de Lys suits Keller's award-winning cuisine, which, although steeped in classical tradition, welcomes the challenge of California's culinary revolution. Designed by the late Michael Taylor, the dining room is draped with hundreds of yards of hand-painted red floral fabric, like an immense garden tent.

AVERAGE DINNER FOR TWO: $70
DOES NOT INCLUDE WINE, TAX AND GRATUITY

VIP

Perrier Art Bottles:
Available in Fine
Dining Establishments
Everywhere.

THE ART OF

BOTTLED IN FRANCE
Perrier®
SPARKLING
MINERAL
WATER

REFRESHMENT

THE FLY TRAP

606 FOLSOM STREET
AT SECOND
SAN FRANCISCO, CA 94107
(415) 243-0580
Visa & Major Credit Cards
Dinner Mon-Fri • Lunch Mon-Fri

Proprietor
GLENN MEYERS

Chef
ROBBY MORGENSTEIN

Recommended Items

Appetizers
CRAB CAKES • OYSTERS
ROCKEFELLER • BRUSCHETTA
WITH WILD MUSHROOMS &
FONTINA • CELERY VICTOR
• WHITE SALAD

Entreès
CHICKEN JERUSALEM
• HANGTOWN FRY • PETIT FILET
ROQUEFORT • OSSO BUCCO
• CASSOULET • MONTEREY
SEAFOOD STEW

IN THE TIME OF HORSE-DRAWN STREETCARS, LOUIE'S RESTAURANT on Market Street was nicknamed "the fly trap" for the squares of fly paper placed on every table by owner Louis Besozzi. After the 1906 earthquake, Louis's cousin Henry opened The Fly Trap on Montgomery, which became a favorite of San Francisco's movers and shakers until it was razed in 1963. ♦ Craig Zolezzi and his father Walter launched the new Fly Trap in 1989. Walter is now the executive chef, helping Chef Robby Morgenstein recreate the famous classics of San Francisco's past, and the dynamic Glenn Meyers is sole proprietor. ♦ What makes the Fly Trap so interesting, and so good, is its ideal marriage of past and present. The restaurant has a turn-of-the-century look, with golden "antiqued" prints in lieu of wallpaper, an original pressed-tin ceiling, Bentwood chairs and wood floors. The staff on the other hand is impressively young and enthusiastic. And the specialities, whether celery Victor, osso bucco or coq au vin, are infused with a '90s emphasis on fresh flavor. This is definitely not a place to skip for dessert, for what better place is there to indulge your nostalgia for a banana split or a warm apple crisp?

AVERAGE DINNER FOR TWO: $50
DOES NOT INCLUDE WINE, TAX AND GRATUITY

VIP

FOG CITY DINER

1300 BATTERY STREET
AT EMBARCADERO
SAN FRANCISCO, CA 94111
(415) 982-2000

Visa, MasterCard, Discover & Diners Club
Open Daily • Lunch & Dinner

Managing Partner
JOE PECK

Chef/Partner
ROBERT CUBBERLY

Recommended Items

Appetizers
VARIOUS FRESH
CHILLED SHELLFISH
• SCALLOPS & MANGO CEVICHE
• GRILLED EGGPLANT WITH
JAPANESE MISO & SCALLIONS

Entrées
ROASTED LEG OF LAMB
SANDWICH WITH WATERCRESS
& TOMATO-APRICOT CHUTNEY
• SPICY SESAME CHICKEN SALAD
• PASTA WITH GRILLED
SCALLOPS, SAFFRON, CREAM &
SWEET PEAS • CRISPY RABBIT
WITH ANCHO CHILI SUCCOTASH

SINCE FOG CITY DINER OPENED IN 1985 WITH A PRECEDENT setting concept of diner-as-sophisticated-restaurant, it has become an icon that defines San Francisco's culinary direction. Accessible food prepared in the open is now an element of many fine city restaurants. ♦ Under the direction of Real Restaurants' Bill Higgins, Bill Upson and Cindy Pawlcyn, Chef/Partner Robert Cubberly keeps the eatery at the head of the restaurant pack. Beyond the landmark chrome-and-neon facade, a streamlined interior complements the innovative diner food centered on small plates made for "grazing," another trendsetting idea that has ignited the country. If you prefer tradition-al diner fare, you won't be disappointed. Modern interpretations of all-American favorites such as chili dogs and milk shakes are also available. Certainly Fog City has spawned a tradition, but don't be fooled – there's no topping the original.

AVERAGE DINNER FOR TWO: $45
DOES NOT INCLUDE WINE, TAX AND GRATUITY

HARRIS'

2100 VAN NESS AVENUE
AT PACIFIC AVENUE
SAN FRANCISCO, CA 94109
(415) 673-1888

Visa & Major Credit Cards
Open Daily • Dinner Only

Proprietor
ANN LEE HARRIS

Chef
GOETZ BOJE

Recommended Items

Appetizers
FRESH OYSTERS
• ESCARGOT
• CAESAR SALAD
• STEAK TARTARE

Entrées
THE HARRIS STEAK
• ROAST PRIME RIB
• GRILLED SALMON
• LAMB CHOPS
• MAINE LOBSTER

POPULAR VOTE RATES HARRIS' ONE OF THE BEST STEAKHOUSES in San Francisco. Midwestern corn-fed beef, dry aged for twenty-one days to develop flavor and tenderness, is the specialty at this handsome, high ceilinged restaurant with comfortable booth seating. A turn-of-the-century bar sets the scene for award-winning martinis while the spacious Skylight Room accomodates private parties of up to 100 guests. ♦ Chef Goetz Boje prepares a wide selection of grilled meats and seafood, and an in-house baker creates the popular decadent chocolate cake and the apple and pecan pies. ♦ The wine list includes an extensive selection of California Cabernets and Merlots, as well as numerous imported wines. For those who want to experience Harris' robust steaks at home, they're available for purchase at the retail meat counter.

AVERAGE DINNER FOR TWO: $85
DOES NOT INCLUDE WINE, TAX AND GRATUITY

VIP

S T E A K H O U S E

HOUSE OF PRIME RIB

1906 VAN NESS AVENUE
NEAR JACKSON
SAN FRANCISCO, CA 94109
(415) 885-4605

Visa & Major Credit Cards
Open Daily • Dinner Only

Proprietor
JOE BETZ

Chef
DIETER CZIRR

Recommended Items

Entrées

KING HENRY VIII CUT
OF PRIME BEEF • HOUSE
OF PRIME RIB CUT • PRIME
RIB À LA CARTE • FRESH
FISH: CATCH OF THE DAY
• ALL PRIME RIB DINNERS
SERVED WITH SALAD,
MASHED OR BAKED
POTATOES, YORKSHIRE
PUDDING, CREAMED
SPINACH & FRESH
HORSERADISH SAUCE

THE HOUSE OF PRIME RIB WAS A SAN FRANCISCO INSTITUTION, under the same management for thirty-eight years. Now it seems headed for another long and prosperous reign under proprietor Joe Betz. ♦ In a complete remodeling, Joe decorated the interior with light, airy pastel colors and added brass-etched glass to recreate the atmosphere of an English pub. The specialty of the kitchen, however, has not changed. Each year at House of Prime Rib, some ninety tons of Eastern corn-fed beef are cured with a secret herb blend from England, packed in rock salt and roasted in seasoned ovens. The result: thick, juicy slices of prime rib, cooked to order and artfully carved from gleaming service carts at the table. ♦ Chef Dieter Czirr prepares each prime rib dinner and the accompaniments, as well as a fresh fish of the day.

AVERAGE DINNER FOR TWO: $45
DOES NOT INCLUDE WINE, TAX AND GRATUITY

VIP

Making Friends
Since 1864

IMPERIAL PALACE

919 GRANT AVENUE
AT WASHINGTON
SAN FRANCISCO, CA 94108
(415) 982-8889

Visa & Major Credit Cards
Open Daily • Lunch & Dinner

Proprietor
TOMMY TOY

Chef
SUN HO

Recommended Items

Appetizers
HONEYDEW PRAWNS
• MINCED BBQ DUCK
Entrées
THAI-SPICED CHICKEN
• PEKING DUCK
• MUSHU PORK
• FRESH LOBSTER OR
CRABIN GINGER &
CHINESE WINE SAUCE
• SICHUAN SEAFOOD
COMBINATION

IN THE HEART OF SAN FRANCISCO'S CHINATOWN IS TOMMY TOY'S famed Imperial Palace, an elegant Chinese setting that has attracted an impressive celebrity clientele for over 35 years. Rich green and gold tones enhance the dining room, where Chinese artifacts from partner Joe Yuey's collection is displayed. The entryway is lined with autographed pictures of the stars who have dined here, including Barbara Streisand, Bette Midler, Clint Eastwood, and Frank Sinatra. ♦ Toy is an energetic impresario, greeting guests and keeping close watch over the kitchen, where Chef Sun Ho oversees the production of authentic Mandarin, Cantonese and Hunan dishes. A mouth-watering selection of Dim Sum is available for lunch. ♦ Like his other fine restaurant, Tommy Toy's Cuisine Chinoise, the Imperial Palace reflects Toy's knowledge and appreciation of wine with a well-balanced selection of California vintages.

AVERAGE DINNER FOR TWO: $40
DOES NOT INCLUDE WINE, TAX AND GRATUITY

ITALIAN

KULETO'S

VILLA FLORENCE HOTEL
221 POWELL STREET
SAN FRANCISCO, CA 94102
(415) 397-7720

Visa & Major Credit Cards
Open Daily • Breakfast, Lunch & Dinner

General Manager
PETE SITTNICK

Executive Chef
ROBERT HELSTROM

Recommended Items

Appetizers
ROASTED GARLIC & CAMBAZOLA WITH ROSEMARY PIZZA BREAD • GRILLED RADICCHIO & PANCETTA

Entrées
BREAST OF CHICKEN STUFFED WITH RICOTTA & HERBS, ROASTED PEPPER BUTTER SAUCE • CAPELLINI WITH ROMA TOMATOES, BASIL & GARLIC • SAFFRON RISOTTO WITH PRAWNS, SCALLOPS & SUNDRIED TOMATOES

KULETO'S IS AN ACTION-PACKED RESTAURANT WITH UP-TO-DATE Italian food and one of the most inviting bars in town. Forty feet of mahogany, it survived the 1906 quake in the Palace Hotel only to be put in storage. Designer Pat Kuleto, for whom the restaurant is named, refurbished it, hung garlic, dried herbs, salamis – even whole hams – above it, and set a warm, spirited tone that never gets tiring. ♦ Kuleto's and the Villa Florence Hotel are owned by Bill Kimpton, the man behind other successful restaurant/hotel duos such as Masa's/Hotel Vintage Court and Corona Bar & Grill/Monticello Inn. After pioneering the menu at Corona, Chef Bob Helstrom was sent to Italy to learn the secrets of Italian cuisine. He cures his own prosciutto, makes mozzarella, vinegar, breads and desserts in house, and buys the best extra-virgin olive oil to set on every table. ♦ "In Italy, I learned that food is best kept simple and natural," he explains. "Here, we are a little more eclectic, but the accent is always on freshness." ♦ The restaurant's new Machiavelli Room accommodates up to fifty for private gatherings.

AVERAGE DINNER FOR TWO: $50
DOES NOT INCLUDE WINE, TAX AND GRATUITY

La Brasserie Française

THREE EMBARCADERO CENTER
SACRAMENTO AT DAVIS
SAN FRANCISCO, CA 94111
(415) 981-5530

Visa & Major Credit Cards
Dinner Daily • Lunch Mon-Fri

Proprietors
RICHARD MOSCONI
BERNARD COLLIN

Executive Chef
STEPHEN GANNER

Recommended Items

Appetizers
GRILLED SESAME GLAZED SHRIMP WITH SOUTHERN-STYLE CORN RELISH & RED PEPPER ESSENCE • OYSTERS ON THE HALF SHELL WITH CARIBBEAN COCKTAIL SAUCE & MIGNONETTE

Entrées
PASSION FRUIT MARINATED SEABASS WITH ROASTED BELL PEPPERS, MANGO, SCALLION & SWEET POTATO FRIES • WHOLE ROASTED RHUM GLAZED POUSSIN WITH ARUGULA, GINGER SUSHI RICE & RED CURRY COCONUT SAUCE

HAILED BY *BON APPETIT* AS "ONE OF THE BEST AND MOST affordable French restaurants in San Francisco," La Brasserie Française has arrived. Owners Richard Mosconi and Bernard Collin brought their past restaurant experience and success from their London restaurant Le Renoir, to San Francisco. In 1994 Chef Stephen Ganner joined the team bringing "New World" Caribbean cooking techniques in addition to his European background. Stephen worked in many respected restaurants including the award winning Handsels Restaurant in Scotland and the Scottish Highland's Orient Express. ♦ Together these three talented individuals have created a restaurant where Paris and French Island marry and beget a distinctly San Franciscan cuisine. Whether it's lunch under the sun amid flowers and trees or a quiet dinner beside the dining room's large fireplace, natives and visitors are basking in the glow of La Brasserie's varied, inexpensive brasserie fare. A good choice is the three-course, prix-fixe meal for $18. ♦ Desserts explore the vast lands of French sweets, and wines are from France and California. If you're looking for a menu of affordable French favorites prepared with creative skill, La Brasserie Française is the place for you.

AVERAGE DINNER FOR TWO: $40
DOES NOT INCLUDE WINE, TAX AND GRATUITY

La Folie

2316 Polk Street
AT GREEN
San Francisco, Ca 94109
(415) 776-5577

Visa & Major Credit Cards
Closed Sunday • Dinner Only

Maître d'
Georges Passot
Proprietor
Jamie Passot

Chef/Proprietor
Roland Passot

Recommended Items

Appetizers
Sautéed Hudson Valley foie
gras, poached pear, wild
huckleberry sauce
• Canneloni of fresh crab &
lobster in leeks & avocado,
mustard vinaigrette

Entrées
Roti of quail & squab
wrapped in crispy potato
strings, natural juice with
truffles • Potato spiral
of sweetbreads & shiitakes,
Port sauce & parsley coulis

WHEN GREAT CHEFS LIKE JULIA CHILD AND PAUL BOCUSE VISIT San Francisco, your likely to find them dining at La Folie. Roland Passot is an artist, not just a chef and he has gathered consistent rave reviews from food critics around the country. La Folie is considered by *Zagat* and *Focus Magazine* among the top three French restaurants in the city. ♦ "I call my cooking spontaneous," says the genial Roland. "I never know what I'm going to prepare until after I call my suppliers." ♦ The dining room, with clouds painted on a blue ceiling and monkeys and parrots cavorting on yellow drapes, is crazy enough to convey the "folly" implied by the restaurant's name, yet as warm and inviting as a family-run restaurant should be. Roland's wife, Jamie, is the friendly hostess. Brother Georges, the maître d' and sommelier, has assembled a unique wine list featuring outstanding, little-known French and California selections at great prices.

AVERAGE DINNER FOR TWO: $75
DOES NOT INCLUDE WINE, TAX AND GRATUITY

La Pergola

2060 CHESTNUT STREET
AT STEINER
SAN FRANCISCO, CA 94123
(415) 563-4500

Visa & Major Credit Cards
Open Daily • Dinner Only

Proprietor
SANDRA SIEBERT

Chef/Proprietor
GIANCARLO
BORTOLOTTI

Recommended Items

Appetizers

TIMBALLO: MOZZARELLA &
MIXED VEGETABLES BAKED &
SERVED IN SPINACH SAUCE
• TRIETTO: SLICED SALMON,
TUNA & SEABASS, RADICCHIO
& ARUGULA

Entrées

CONIGLIO: SONOMA RABBIT
BAKED IN VEGETABLE
SAUCE, SOFT POLENTA
• PASTA FILLED WITH SQUASH
IN BUTTER & SAGE
SAUCE

"WHEN I WAS A BOY, MY MOTHER HAD NO TIME TO COOK, SO she taught me how," says Chef/Owner Giancarlo Bortolotti. Necessity soon turned to passion, and today, although he is far from his childhood village, his uncompromised regional fare remains close to home. ♦ With the help of his wife, Sandra Siebert, Giancarlo creates La Pergola's lighthearted atmosphere. Yet he is very serious when it comes to his kitchen, often perfecting a recipe for months before putting it on his seasonal menu. Once a week Giancarlo travels up the Northern California coast to hand pick organically grown produce, the finest mushrooms and freshest eggs imaginable. Says Chef Giancarlo, "I especially like to design meals for customers who leave their food and wine selections to me." Diners can also rely on him to keep fat usage to a minimum. ♦ The mostly Italian wine cellar is stocked with unusual vintages and great values served at the restaurant's casual, European bar or in the uncluttered dining room with soothing sponge-painted walls and dimmed track lights.

AVERAGE DINNER FOR TWO: $50
DOES NOT INCLUDE WINE, TAX AND GRATUITY

VIP

Ooooh, Je t'aime!

MOËT & CHANDON
CHAMPAGNE
ÉPERNAY ★ FRANCE

WHERE CELEBRATION IS BORN™

LE CENTRAL

453 BUSH STREET
AT GRANT
SAN FRANCISCO, CA 94108
(415) 391-2233

Visa & Major Credit Cards
Closed Sunday • Lunch & Dinner

Proprietor
CLAUDE CAPPELLE

Chef
PAUL TANPHANICH

Recommended Items

Appetizers
FRESH CELERY ROOT
REMOULADE • FRESH
LEEKS VINAIGRETTE • CRAB
CAKES BEURRE BLANC • WARM
GARLIC SAUSAGE, POTATOES
WITH VINAIGRETTE

Entrées
PAILLARD OF CHICKEN
WITH PASTA • CASSOULET
"LE CENTRAL"
• CHOUCROUTE A
L'ALSACIENNE • FILET
MIGNON AU POIVRE
• BOUDIN NOIR • COLD
SALMON WITH SAUCE VERTE

LE CENTRAL – TWENTY YEARS AGO , THE FIRST BRASSERIE TO open in San Francisco. Today, walk through the door and be warmly greeted by Maitre d' Michel Bonnet. Feel as if you're being transported to France – brick walls, mirrors, hand-written chalkboard menus, fresh-cut flowers. An atmosphere that is lively yet intimate. ♦ A menu of classic bistro-style dishes, all expertly prepared by Chefs John and Paul Tanphanich. Want more choices? A chalkboard offering daily specials – seasonal items such as a salad of freshly roasted beet or contemporary entrées with a California touch. Can't make up your mind about the appetizer? Order an assortment of whatever tempts you. Some wine? Choose from a carefully selected list of French and California vintages. Finally, a choice of tempting desserts, a coffee, an after-dinner drink – the perfect end to your dining experience. ♦ You have shared in the Le Central tradition that owners Michel, John, and Paul, their dedicated staff, and the restaurant's founders, brothers Claude and Pierre Cappelle have nurtured and maintained – a tradition of excellence recognized by the coveted 1994 DiRona Award. Thank you for joining us!

AVERAGE DINNER FOR TWO: $60
DOES NOT INCLUDE WINE, TAX AND GRATUITY

ORDER YOUR COPY OF EPICUREAN RENDEZVOUS TODAY!

☐ YES! Please send me Epicurean Rendezvous for only $4.95 plus $3.00 for postage & handling, a total of $7.95 for EACH copy ordered.

__NEW YORK __CHICAGO __SOUTHERN CALIFORNIA __NORTHERN CALIFORNIA __ FLORIDA
(PLEASE INDICATE HOW MANY OF EACH)

Mail Orders to:

EPICUREAN RENDEZVOUS
3850 NORTH WILKE ROAD, SUITE 250
ARLINGTON HEIGHTS, ILLINOIS 60004

ORDER YOUR COPY OF EPICUREAN RENDEZVOUS TODAY!

☐ YES! Please send me Epicurean Rendezvous' Special Anniversary Edition which includes all five markets:(New York, Chicago, Southern California, Northern California & Florida) for only $12.95 plus $4.00 for postage & handling, for a total of $16.95 for EACH copy ordered.

____EPICUREAN RENDEZVOUS SPECIAL ANNIVERSARY EDITION
(PLEASE INDICATE HOW MANY OF EACH)

Mail Orders to:

EPICUREAN RENDEZVOUS
3850 NORTH WILKE ROAD, SUITE 250
ARLINGTON HEIGHTS, ILLINOIS 60004

PLEASE MAIL THIS CARD IN AN ENVELOPE TO:

EPICUREAN RENDEZVOUS

3850 NORTH WILKE ROAD, SUITE 250
ARLINGTON HEIGHTS, ILLINOIS 60004

Name _____

Address _____

City _____ State _____ Zip _____

❒ Check Enclosed

❒ Charge to: ❒ Visa   ❒ MasterCard   ❒ American Express

Card # _____ Exp. _____

Signature _____

Sorry, we do not bill. Please allow 3 to 4 weeks for delivery. Foreign orders, add $20 U.S. currency.
Illinois residents add 8% sales tax.

PLEASE MAIL THIS CARD IN AN ENVELOPE TO:

EPICUREAN RENDEZVOUS

3850 NORTH WILKE ROAD, SUITE 250
ARLINGTON HEIGHTS, ILLINOIS 60004

Name _____

Address _____

City _____ State _____ Zip _____

❒ Check Enclosed

❒ Charge to: ❒ Visa   ❒ MasterCard   ❒ American Express

Card # _____ Exp. _____

Signature _____

Sorry, we do not bill. Please allow 3 to 4 weeks for delivery. Foreign orders, add $20 U.S. currency.
Illinois residents add 8% sales tax.

Le Club

1250 JONES
AT CLAY
SAN FRANCISCO, CA 94109
(415) 771-5400

Visa & Major Credit Cards
Dinner Only • Tues-Sun

Manager
PATRICK BOMBARD

Chef/Proprietor
YVES GARNIER

Recommended Items

Appetizers
BASIL-ROASTED SCAMPI
• ROSES OF MELON, PARMA
HAM & AGED PORT SORBET

Entrées
GRILLED SEABASS, TOMATO
BASIL SAFFRON MARMELADE,
CITRON RISOTTO
• MAINE LOBSTER
FRICASSÉE, BASMATI RICE,
YOUNG VEGETABLES
• ROASTED LAMB RACK WITH
VEGETABLES MONTE CARLO

TRUE TO ITS NAME, EVERYTHING AT LE CLUB SMACKS OF exclusivity. Beyond the plush entrance, burnished mahogany paneling, glittering chandeliers and antique French beveled black glass in the small dining rooms are all new. The gorgeous, clubby bar seats ten. Perched atop Nob Hill within the Clay-Jones apartment complex since 1947, the private club went public in 1967. The latest reincartion may be the most exquisite, yet it caters to the tastes and budgets of today's dinners. ♦ Featuring two prix fixe dinners at startlingly low prices, Superchef and Owner Yves Garnier creates what he calls "Cuisine du Soleil," covering a wide area of the Mediterranean including France, Italy and other countries. "The real heart is the seasonal freshness of my ingredients and a marriage of the best of the old and new." ♦ Every window is kept tightly shuttered a self-contained environment. Low ceilings and original etchings by Picasso and Matisse lend a pleasantly conspiratorial air. The wine list is heavy on reds with extensive Cabernet and red Bordeaux selections. Desserts are reinventions of "Old World" classics.

AVERAGE DINNER FOR TWO: $60
DOES NOT INCLUDE WINE, TAX AND GRATUITY

L'OLIVIER

465 DAVIS STREET
NEAR JACKSON
SAN FRANCISCO, CA 94111
(415) 981-7824

Visa & Major Credit Cards
Dinner Mon-Sat • Lunch Mon-Fri

Proprietor
CHRISTIAN FRANCOZ

Proprietor
GUY FRANCOZ

Recommended Items

Appetizers
SEAFOOD SAUSAGE
• FEUILLETÉ OF LOBSTER
WITH SAUTERNES

Entrées
SPECIALTY OF BOUILLABAISSE,
MARSEILLES STYLE
• RABBIT CASSEROLE
• ROASTED DUCKLING
WITH ORANGE SAUCE
• STUFFED BREAST OF CHICKEN
WITH SHIITAKES &
RED BELL PEPPERS

CELEBRATING ITS SIXTEENTH ANNIVERSARY, L'OLIVIER IS AS popular as ever for anyone seeking an exceptional lunch or a very romantic dinner. The main dining room, decorated with French antiques, exudes a quiet, inviting grace and opens on to a large greenhouse filled with plants and fresh flowers. This airy room's elegantly casual ambiance is the perfect complement to the more formal main room. ♦ The kitchen creates recipes that borrow from a diverse background. This, integrated with traditional French technique, makes for some very inventive dishes. Desserts are superbly rich, and include a delectable soufflé and signature crème brulée. ♦ L'Olivier's wine list is a pleasure to peruse featuring the most current California selections as well as renowned French vintages.

AVERAGE DINNER FOR TWO: $56
DOES NOT INCLUDE WINE, TAX AND GRATUITY

Baume & Mercier & Me

18K gold diamond-set bracelet watch from the Classiques Collection.
Twelve diamonds mark the hours on a mother-of-pearl dial.

Φ

BAUME & MERCIER
GENEVE

Classiques
(enlarged)

SHREVE & CO.

SAN FRANCISCO'S JEWELER SINCE 1852

POST & GRANT, SAN FRANCISCO (415) 421-2600 · (800) 5-SHREVE
STANFORD SHOPPING CENTER, PALO ALTO (415) 327-2211
BROADWAY PLAZA, WALNUT CREEK (510) 937-0900

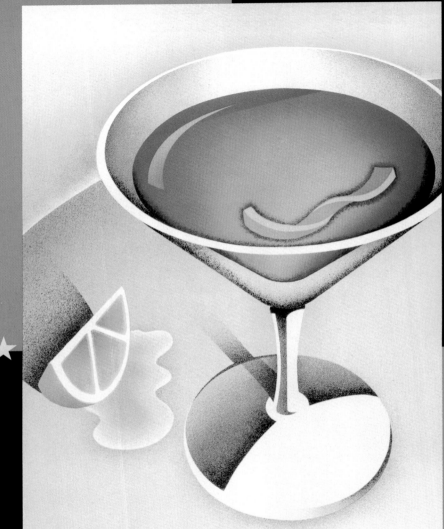

HENNESSY
Martini

Discover this classic. Combine 2 oz. of Hennessy V.S and a squeeze of lemon over ice.
Stir gently, don't shake. Strain into a chilled martini glass. Or ask your bartender.

MASA'S

648 BUSH STREET
NEAR STOCKTON
SAN FRANCISCO, CA 94108
(415) 989-7154 • 1-800-258-7694

Visa & Major Credit Cards
Closed Sunday & Monday • Dinner Only

Manager
JAMES SOULÉ

Chef
JULIAN SERRANO

Recommended Items

Appetizers
FOIE GRAS SAUTÉE WITH
MADEIRA TRUFFLE SAUCE
• LOBSTER SALAD WITH
JULIENNE OF CRISP-FRIED
LEEK & SAFFRON
INFUSED POTATOES

Entrées
RACK OF LAMB WITH
POTATO ONION TART &
CARAWAY CUMIN
SAUCE • MEDALLIONS
OF VENISON WITH
CARAMELIZED APPLES &
ZINFANDEL SAUCE

THE MEMORY OF MASTER CHEF MASATAKA KOBAYASHI GUIDES Chef Julian Serrano as he carries on the visual and gastronomic artistry at Masa's. Together with manager James Soulé and Owner Bill Kimpton, Serrano has maintained the impeccable standards set by Masa. Trained in Madrid, Serrano worked with Masa for three years: "I express myself within the unique style and tradition he set." ♦ The magic at Masa's is a combination of aesthetic flair and outstanding cooking; there is so much on each plate, so carefully presented, that it takes at least sixteen people in the kitchen to create fewer than 100 dinners each night. Chef Serrano's daily tasting menu is a great way to sample a little of everything, and even better when complemented by Sommelier Burke Owens's wine suggestions specially designed to go with it. ♦ Masa's regular wine list is outstanding, and a modest bar serves an extensive Californian and French selection. Where else could you find Château d'Yquem by the glass?

AVERAGE DINNER FOR TWO: $136
DOES NOT INCLUDE WINE, TAX AND GRATUITY

VIP

MacArthur Park

607 Front Street
AT JACKSON
San Francisco, CA 94111
(415) 398-5700
Visa & Major Credit Cards
Open Daily for Dinner • Lunch Mon-Fri

General Manager
JEFF HANEK

Chef
LUIS A. PEREZ

Recommended Items

Appetizers

BLUE CORN-FRIED OYSTERS
W/TOMATILLO SALSA & CHIPO-
TLE CREAM • BAKED GOAT
CHEESE SALAD W/HERBS,
BREADCRUMBS, FIELD GREENS
& PEAR-SHERRY VINAIGRETTE

Entrées

AWARD-WINNING BARBECUED
BABY BACK RIBS W/COLE SLAW
& CHOICE OF POTATO
• BREADED TURKEY CUTLET
STUFFED W/SMITHFIELD HAM,
MUSHROOMS & GRUYERE,
W/MASHED POTATOES & GREEN
BEANS • WHOLE FRIED GINGER-
STUFFED CATFISH, W/SPINACH,
RICE & DIPPING SAUCES

FOR GREAT BARBECUE, SAN FRANCISCANS KNOW THAT ONLY MacArthur Park will do. Since 1972, diners have satisfied their craving for ribs, chicken and sausage at this classic restaurant. The honest American cuisine, with a range of mesquite-grilled meat, fish and fowl, has never lost its appeal. Appetizers spice up the creative American menu, and outstanding salads include a fine Caesar and a hearty traditional Cobb. Portions are generous, with first-rate ingredients and a variety of creative accompaniments in addition to good old mashed potatoes. ♦ Another reason for MacArthur Park's enduring popularity is its warm, bustling atmosphere. Located on Walton Park in the historical Jackson Square district, the restaurant is in a renovated warehouse from the early 1900s. Large and high-ceilinged, with plenty of wood and brick, it has a 60-foot bar, several dining areas and three private rooms – all usually crowded with an interesting mix of people. During the day, a take-out counter sees a lot of action. Regulars fax in their orders, and business lunchers from the nearby Financial District schmooze over state-of-the-art hamburgers. At night, a younger crowd takes over the bar, while singles, families and couples dine in noisy splendor.

AVERAGE DINNER FOR TWO: $50
DOES NOT INCLUDE WINE, TAX AND GRATUITY

THE MANDARIN

900 NORTH POINT
GHIRARDELLI SQUARE
SAN FRANCISCO, CA 94109
(415) 673-8812

Visa & Major Credit Cards
Open Daily • Lunch & Dinner

Proprietor
JULIAN MAO

Executive Chef
KENNY LIU

Recommended Items

Appetizers
MANDARIN SPARERIBS
• CRAB CLAWS • MANDARIN
MINCED SQUAB

Entrées
BLACK PEPPER BEEF • SMOKED
TEA DUCK • MONGOLIAN
FIRE POT • GLAZED WALNUT
PRAWNS • PEKING DUCK
• GLAZED TROPICAL FRUIT
• DAILY SPECIALS THAT PAIR
SUCH NOVELTY INGREDIENTS
AS WILD RICE WITH SESAME-
INFUSED JELLYFISH, A
REFRESHINGLY COOL DISH

GHIRADELLI SQUARE, THE FORMER CHOCOLATE FACTORY NEAR Fisherman's Wharf, is home to the Mandarin, one of San Francisco's most beautiful restaurants and the first restaurant in the United States to serve Szechwan and Northern Chinese cuisine. Huge pillars, quarried floor tiles, luxurious Oriental carpets, stone and wood-hewn statues, and rotating fine art exhibits recall the grandeur of imperial China. ♦ This palace setting is the perfect backdrop for Mao's world-famous cuisine. Born to an aristocratic family in Nanking, Mao received his culinary training through apprenticeship as well as in the family kitchen, where elegant state banquets were regularly produced. In 1990, when the Mandarin's former owners announced their intention to retire, Mao, the restaurant's general manager for 15 years, purchased the establishment. Today, the Mandarin's character is made even richer by Mao's distinctive signature touch. ♦ The kitchen's repertoire of over 300 dishes offers a one-stop tour of the Orient's finest. Executive Chef Kenny Liu adds a unique style he calls "New Wave Hong Kong," centering on East-meets-West cuisine themes.

AVERAGE DINNER FOR TWO: $45
DOES NOT INCLUDE WINE, TAX AND GRATUITY

McCormick & Kuleto's

900 NORTH POINT STREET
SAN FRANCISCO, CA 94109
(415) 929-1730

Visa & Major Credit Cards
Open Daily • Lunch & Dinner

General Manager
LAURA MATHEWS

Senior Chef
REÑE VAN BROEKHUIZEN
Chef de Cuisine
STUART SMITH

Recommended Items

Appetizers
WESTCOTT BAY BELON OYSTERS
• DUNGENESS CRABCAKES
• ROMAINE SALAD WITH
ANCHOVY-GARLIC DRESSING

Entrées
MESQUITE GRILLED ATLANTIC
SALMON WITH BABY LEEKS &
SPICY BLOOD ORANGE COULIS
• HAWAIIAN SWORDFISH
WITH PINEAPPLE TAMARIND
BASTE, CRISPY GINGER &
FRIED SHRIMP CHIPS
• PACIFIC SEAFOOD STEW WITH
CRAB, MUSSELS, PRAWNS &
MANILA CLAMS

THE SPECTACULAR DESIGN OF McCORMICK & KULETO'S BRINGS one of the world's most incredible views to every table in the restaurant. Brilliant in the morning sun, mysterious when the fog rolls in and crowned by lights at night, the Golden Gate Bridge, Aquatic Park and the hills across the bay are ever fascinating. The restaurant that is "bringing locals back to the waterfront" offers more than a water's edge vision, however. ♦ The modestly priced menu boasts more than thirty varieties of fresh seafood from Mexico to Cape Cod and everyplace north, south, east, and west. Delivered by McCormick & Kuleto's own wholesale fish company, the daily catch is chosen by Senior Chef René Van Broekhuizen, who quips, "From 6AM to 9AM, I feel like a commodities buyer." Choices include mesquite-grilled specialties, oyster bar bounty and brick-oven pizza served at the Crab Cake Lounge – an informal area within the restaurant. With the Napa Valley next door, the wine list is world-class.

AVERAGE DINNER FOR TWO: $40
DOES NOT INCLUDE WINE, TAX AND GRATUITY

MOOSE'S

1652 STOCKTON STREET
SAN FRANCISCO, CA 94133
(415) 989-7800

Visa & Major Credit Cards
Dinner Daily • Lunch Tues-Sat • Sunday Brunch

Proprietor
ED MOOSE

Executive Chef
MARC VALIANI

Recommended Items

Appetizers

HEARTH OVEN-ROASTED
SHELLFISH WITH SWEET
SHALLOT-PARSLEY BROTH
• PARMESAN-BUTTER RISOTTO
WITH ARTICHOKE RAGOUT

Entreés

SALMON & POACHED OYSTERS
WITH PASTA PEARLS, SALSIFY
& TARRAGON-SHRIMP BROTH
• HEARTH OVEN-ROASTED
DUCK WITH "BURNT" HONEY-
GINGER SAUCE & WILD MUSH-
ROOM SPRING ROLL

WHEN IT COMES TO CREATING A WARM AMBIANCE, ED MOOSE IS A master. Moose's welcomes from afar. The electric blue light of its neon cartoon moose beckons one and all to the convivial bar and comfortable tables of this lively North Beach bistro. Modeled after the great European cafés it combines vaulting Sienna-beige walls, streetside floor-to-ceiling windows, a bustling exhibition kitchen and select piano jazz for an unpretentious atmosphere that is right for any occasion. ♦ Now Moose's many patrons have more reason to celebrate: the cuisine of Chef Marc Valiani has made a top-ranked restaurant even better. Formerly chef at Rox in Beverly Hills, Valiani earned his credentials with Wolfgang Puck at Spago and Eureka, George Morrone at Hotel Bel Air and Dean Fearing at the Mansion on Turtle Creek in Dallas. His bold, beautiful combinations showcase fresh regional products, with a wide range of appetizers, entrees, pastas, pizza and risotto. ♦ Moose's wine steward has put together a stellar selection of American and European wines to pair with Valiani's distinct contemporary style.

AVERAGE DINNER FOR TWO: $50
DOES NOT INCLUDE WINE, TAX AND GRATUITY

MORTON'S OF CHICAGO

400 POST STREET
AT POWELL
SAN FRANCISCO, CA 94102
(415) 986-5830

Visa & Major Credit Cards
Open Daily for Dinner • Lunch Mon-Fri

General Manager
BRENDA ESQUIBELL

Chef
LUGARDO BERNAL

Recommended Items

Appetizers
• JUMBO SEA SCALLOPS IN BACON
• SHRIMP CHEF ALEXANDER
• SMOKED PACIFIC SALMON

Entrées
• 24-OUNCE AGED PORTERHOUSE STEAK
• NEW YORK SIRLOIN STRIP STEAK
• SICILIAN VEAL CHOP

DOWN A FLIGHT OF BLUE-CARPETED STAIRS, MORTON'S OF Chicago has the traditional elegance usually associated with an established private club. Mahogany dominates the decor, with white tablecloths on big round tables and spacious booth seating. Celebrity photos and historical prints line the walls and brass-plated private wine lockers, and a large bar add to the feeling of comfort. ♦ With its ambiance of old-fashioned pampering, it's hard to believe Morton's has only been in San Francisco since 1994. First opened in Chicago in 1978, Morton's is now popular in 30 locations for good reason: beef, the very best available, is served with one-pound baked potatoes, fresh accompaniments and sophisticated desserts. Portions are generous. A 24-ounce Porterhouse, a 20-ounce New York sirloin and a 14-ounce double-cut filet are among the popular cuts. ♦ As important as the quality of the food is the first-class service. At Morton's, the staff caters to diners with polished personal attention. Add a far-ranging, well-priced wine list to the formula, and you understand why Morton's has earned such a loyal clientele. This is already proving true in San Francisco, where a dose of Heartland dining is a welcome change of pace.

AVERAGE DINNER FOR TWO: $80
DOES NOT INCLUDE WINE, TAX AND GRATUITY

· EST · 1822 ·

FONSECA GUIMARAENS
VINHOS S.A.

· OPORTO · PORTUGAL ·

FONSECA
BIN Nº 27

Fine Reserve

PORT

BOTTLED IN OPORTO   PRODUCT OF PORTUGAL

AMERICAN

ONE MARKET

1 MARKET STREET
SAN FRANCISCO, CA 94105
(415) 777-5577

Visa & Major Credit Cards
Dinner Daily • Lunch Mon-Fri • Sunday Brunch

Chef/Owner
BRADLEY M OGDEN
Owner
MICHAEL D. DELLAR

Chef
ANTHONY D'ONOFRIO
General Manager
QUINN H. MCKENNA

Recommended Items

Appetizers
STEAK TARTARE W/ROCK CRAB,
SUNDRIED TOMATO ROUILLE &
ANCHOVY PARSLEY TOAST
• HOMEGROWN TOMATO SALAD
W/LOCAL GOAT CHEESE

Entrées
OAK-GRILLED CHICKEN BREAST,
WILD RICE SALAD & PANCETTA
WRAPPED PEACHES
• NIMAN-SCHELL BONE-IN
NEW YORK STRIP STEAK
W/WILD MUSHROOM
HASH & FOIE GRAS BUTTER
• COURT BOUILLON POACHED
SALMON W/STEAMED CLAMS,
FENNEL & SALSA VERDE

ONE MARKET IS AN ALL-AMERICAN RESTAURANT LOCATED ON A busy corner of one of America's greatest cities. Set in the historic 1917 Southern Pacific Building, it exudes cosmopolitan vitality. Floor-to-ceiling windows permit a knock-out urban view featuring the Ferry Building. The tastefully appointed dining room is an exciting blur of scurrying waiters accented by the sounds of live jazz piano in the evening. With the restaurant poised at a public transportation hub, the action outside mirrors the interior bustle. ♦ "We focus on farm-fresh, seasonal food that reflects the diversity of American culture, updated and refined," explain Owners Michael Dellar And Bradely Ogden (voted Best Chef-California by the James Beard Society). In other words, like the nation, the restaurant is a melting pot, in this case, of culinary ideas. Complementing the menu, a 500 wine cellar contains many great American bottlings. A special treat: You can reserve a table for up to seven in the restaurant's spectacular open kitchen.

AVERAGE DINNER FOR TWO: $70
DOES NOT INCLUDE WINE, TAX AND GRATUITY

VIP

ORITALIA

1915 FILLMORE STREET
AT PINE
SAN FRANCISCO, CA 94115
(415) 346-1333
Visa & Major Credit Cards
Open Daily • Dinner Only

Proprietor
NORI YOSHIDA

Executive Chef
BRUCE HILL

Recommended Items

Entrées

FRIED SHRIMP &
PORK DUMPLINGS WITH
CILANTRO-MINT SAUCE
• TUNA TARTARE ON
STICKY RICE CAKES
• GRILLED PORTOBELLO
MUSHROOMS, PLUM WINE
JUS • POTATO GNOCCHI WITH
GULF ROCK SHRIMP & GINGER
SAUCE • SEAFOOD MU-SHU,
WHOLE WHEAT MANDARIN
PANCAKES

SIX MONTHS BEFORE HE OPENED ORITALIA'S DOORS TO THE public, Nori Yoshida and his chefs were in the kitchen refining his unique blend of Oriental and Italian cuisines. He teamed linguini with unagi, shiitake mushrooms with sundried tomatoes, and Chinese noodles with balsamic vinegar and olive oil. The results were both satisfying and exotic. Nori and new Executive Chef Bruce Hill, formerly of Aqua, Stars and the Four Seasons Clift, have created an eclectic menu that emphasizes a blend of East and West. They have added many new entrées to the established dishes traditionally served in small portions, such as dim sum and tapas, for the ultimate "grazing" experience. ♦ A man of insatiable culinary curiosity, Nori travels extensively in search of intriguing flavors. "I consider myself a professional food sampler rather than a restaurateur," says the former owner of Yoshida-Ya. "Since I couldn't find anything like this, I created it myself." ♦ Nori masterminded the restaurant's design as well, a classic interior warmed by a huge copper hood over an open kitchen.

AVERAGE DINNER FOR TWO: $50
DOES NOT INCLUDE WINE, TAX AND GRATUITY

PACIFIC
THE PAN PACIFIC HOTEL
500 POST STREET
AT MASON
SAN FRANCISCO, CA 94102
(415) 929-2087
Visa & Major Credit Cards
Open Daily • Breakfast, Lunch & Dinner

Manager
ANIEL CHOPRA

Chef
TAKAYOSHI KAWAI

Recommended Items

Appetizers
FRESH SONOMA FOIE GRAS
SAUTÉ WITH CARAMELIZED
APPLES & CALVADOS SAUCE
• GRILLED LOBSTER IN SHELL
WITH PASTA, VEGETABLE &
LOBSTER JUS
Entrées
STUFFED HERB CHICKEN
BREAST WITH JARDINIERE
VEGETABLES • FILET MIGNON
WITH CRISPY POTATO PANCAKE
& WILD MUSHROOM SAUCE
• DUCK BREAST WITH
CORN CREPES, SPINACH &
WILD BERRY SAUCE

IF LUXURY IS WHAT YOU WANT AND FRIENDLINESS IS WHAT YOU need, Pacific fits the bill. Tucked into the marble opulence of The Pan Pacific Hotel, this restaurant's setting is as fitting for formal wear as it is for a casual rendezvous after work. Here, you can dine regally on foie gras and filet mignon, or feast on an incredible prix-fixe menu for a mere $29. ♦ Always an elegant restaurant, Pacific has become a culinary destination since Chef Takayoshi Kawai came on board. After eight years as sous chef at Masa's, Taka, as he is known, is a master of technique and creativity. His impeccable standards demand the freshest ingredients, and his style emphasizes beauty of presentation and depth of flavor. That extends to the desserts, which include a stellar crème brulée and a sublime chocolate and lime Napoleon. ♦ Pacific may be the best place for a pre- or post-theatre meal, since the location is ideal, the service gracious, and the ambiance worthy of a special evening. The wine list is exemplary, but what is most impressive is the more than twenty wines by the glass, all first rate.

AVERAGE DINNER FOR TWO: $80
DOES NOT INCLUDE WINE, TAX AND GRATUITY

VIP

PALIO D'ASTI

640 SACRAMENTO STREET
AT MONTGOMERY
SAN FRANCISCO, CA 94111
(415) 395-9800

Visa & Major Credit Cards
Dinner Mon-Sat • Lunch Mon-Fri

Proprietor
GIANNI FASSIO

Chef
CRAIG STOLL

Recommended Items

Appetizers
GRILLED PORTOBELLO
MUSHROOM SALAD • MUSSELS
STEAMED WITH WHITE WINE
IN THE WOOD-BURNING OVEN

Entrées
RISOTTO WITH ASPARAGUS &
WHITE TRUFFLE ESSENCE
• SAFFRON GNOCCHI WITH
SWEET PEAS & SAGE BUTTER
• MEZZELUNE FILLED WITH
FONTINA & TOASTED ALMONDS
• CRISPY GRILLED CHICKEN
WITH BALSAMIC VINEGAR
• PAN-FRIED VEAL CHOP
WITH MARSALA SAUCE

PALIO D'ASTI WAS CREATED BY OWNER GIANNI FASSIO AS A restaurant that embodies his vision of Italy: grounded in tradition, yet on the cutting edge of style. The restaurant's theme, a bareback horse race (*il palio*) held in Fassio's ancestral home of Asti since 1275, echoes playfully throughout the award-winning interior: in the bar curved like a racetrack, in the rough stone columns that evoke the streets of Asti, and in the muted medieval colors at play on the surfaces and festive banners. ◆ From San Francisco's sleekest open kitchen comes cuisine as riveting as the design. Chef Craig Stoll designs seasonal menus featuring traditional dishes with particular emphasis on the northern regions of Piedmont and Tuscany, the regions where he studied and worked. Piedmont is noted for its antipasti and risottos while Tuscany is best known for its fish, roasts and vegetarian dishes. An extensive array of antipasti is presented nightly along with a risotto and at least three fresh fish choices. Pastry Chef Jeff Forman's tiramisu is renowned and there is never a lack of chocolate and fresh fruit specials.

AVERAGE DINNER FOR TWO: $40
DOES NOT INCLUDE WINE, TAX AND GRATUITY

POSTRIO

545 POST STREET
NEAR MASON
SAN FRANCISCO, CA 94102
(415) 776-7825
Visa • Major Credit Cards
Open Daily • Breakfast, Lunch & Dinner • Sunday Brunch

General Manager
JACK MOORE

Co-Executive Chefs
STEVEN H. ROSENTHAL
MITCHELL D. ROSENTHAL

Recommended Items

Appetizers
SAUTÉED SCALLOPS W/GREEN
CURRY & KABOCHSA SQUASH
• SAUTÉED FOIE GRAS W/PEAR
VER JUS, WALNUT TOAST AND
TANGERINE COMPOTE

Entrées
GRILLED SQUAB W/SWEET
POTATO FOIE GRAS SPRINGROLL
& BLACKBERRY SAUCE • TUNA
STEAK GRILLED RARE W/CRISPY
NOODLE SALAD & MUSTARD
CURRY SAUCE

DAZZLING CUISINE, CELEBRITY CLIENTELE, CRITICALLY acclaimed chefs, artful ambiance. These are the ingredients that combine the dynamic San Francisco establishment that is Postrio. Since opening in April 1989, Wolfgang Puck's Northern California restaurant maintains a strong local clientele and continues to garner international acclaim. The success and the continuing excitement generated by the menu at Postrio is the direct result of the combined energies of Wolfgang Puck, Steven and Mitchell Rosenthal. The seasonal menus consistently showcase the freshest and finest ingredients while satisfying a variety of taste. The concentration is on California cuisine with a layering of Asian and Mediterranean influences. ◆ Postrio, which is adjacent to the Prescott Hotel on Post Street, is just a block and a half from Union Square. Breakfast, lunch and dinner are served Monday-Friday; brunch and dinner on Saturday and Sunday.

AVERAGE DINNER FOR TWO: $80
DOES NOT INCLUDE WINE, TAX AND GRATUITY

Please don't make this your first bottle o

BY APPOINTMENT TO
HER MAJESTY THE QUEEN SCOTCH WHISKY DISTILLERS
JOHN WALKER AND SONS LTD.

Johnnie Walker.
Blue Label
SCOTCH WHISKY
DISTILLED, BLENDED & BOTTLED BY
JOHN WALKER & SONS
KILMARNOCK SCOTLAND

After all, nobody sta
War and Peace. Nobody pic
and walks right into Wimble
nobody starts drinking Scot
Johnnie Walker Blue.

A recreation of the orig
Johnnie Walker blend, it's c
small number of rare 15 to 6
malts. Sold in an authentic r
the original blue-green cork
available in such limited qua
bottle is given its own numb

So, while we heartily di
from starting out with Johnn
please remember it is an exce

PARK GRILL

PARK HYATT SAN FRANCISCO
333 BATTERY STREET
SAN FRANCISCO, CA 94111
(415) 296-2933

Visa & Major Credit Cards
Breakfast, Lunch & Dinner Daily • Sat & Sun Brunch

General Manager
TONI KNORR

Chef
CHARLES LEWIS

Recommended Items

Appetizers
AHI NAPOLEON W/WONTON
CRISP, AVOCADO & MANGO
VINAIGRETTE • GRILLED POR-
TOBELLO MUSHROOMS
W/ROSEMARY JUS • HEARTS OF
PALM W/PRAWN, ROASTED RED
PEPPER VINAIGRETTE

Entrées
BASIL & SAUSAGE RISOTTO,
ROASTED LOBSTER • OVEN-
ROASTED PORK CHOP, SMOKED
TOMATO CREAM & YELLOW
FINN POTATOES • PAN-SEARED
PACIFIC SALMON, SEMOLINA
CRUSTED ARTICHOKES

GUESTS WHO APPRECIATE COMFORT, WARMTH AND QUIET sophistication have discovered San Francisco's Park Hyatt. The Park Grill exudes the same qualities. Australian lacewood, intricate teak and ebony marquetry, and subtly whimsical still lifes create a relaxing backdrop for Chef Charles Lewis's contemporary California cuisine. ♦ Its proximity to the Financial District and the Embarcadero Center makes the Park Grill a natural choice for power lunches (and breakfasts), post-work cocktails or leisurely dining. Since the outcome of a business meeting can often hinge on the success of the meal itself, the Grill provides personal, professional service – and memo pads at each table. Designed with acoustics in mind, the dining room is never noisy, even when filled to capacity. ♦ For those who are on a less demanding schedule, the Grill also serves a daily menu of light fare from 11 a.m. to 1 a.m. in the bar, a traditional afternoon tea, and early evening caviar and oyster service in the lounge.

AVERAGE DINNER FOR TWO: $70
DOES NOT INCLUDE WINE, TAX AND GRATUITY

PREGO

200 UNION ST.
AT BUCHANAN
SAN FRANCISCO, CA 94123
(415) 563-3305
Visa & Major Credit Cards
Open Daily • Lunch & Dinner

General Manager
MICHELE LAVECCHIA

Chef
LUCA LOFFREDO

Recommended Items

Appetizers

GRILLED TOASTS W/SAUTEED
MUSHROOMS • GRILLED SHRIMP
SALAD W/ARTICHOKES, ARUGU-
LA, CHICK PEAS, LEMON VINAI-
GRETTE • FRIED ZUCCHINI
MARINATED IN VINEGAR, BASIL,
MINT & GARLIC

Entrées

PIZZA W/PARMA PROSCIUTTO,
ASPARAGUS, MOZZARELLA,
GRANA PADANO CHEESE
• PAPPARDELLE PASTA
W/BRAISED RABBIT, VEGETABLES,
RED WINE, MUSHROOMS
• BRAISED VEAL W/BLACK PEP-
PER SAVOY CABBAGE, RED BEETS
& CARAMELIZED BABY ONIONS

SINCE IT OPENED IN 1981, PREGO HAS BEEN A MAGNET FOR STYLISH people who enjoy its European ambiance as much they do its regional Italian food. One of the few restaurants in San Francisco to stay open until midnight, it is urbane and sophisticated. And thanks to a gregarious, largely Italian staff, Prego is a friendly place to dine. ♦ Prego is divided in two by a long, busy bar. On the bar side are several tables for casual dining; on the other is the dining room, with comfortable banquette seating and high-tech hanging lights. Salmon walls, an open kitchen with ceramic tile insets, and a brick wood-burning oven provide a rustic contrast. Floor-to-ceiling windows face bustling Union Street, where tables are set on sunny days. ♦ Prego is famous not only for people-watching, but also for light, straightforward Italian food that defies trends. A dozen *antipasti*, ideal for late-night snacking, focus on vegetables, fresh, grilled and marinated. There are eight kinds of pizza, from a simple *Margherita* to a luscious *calzone* filled with housemade sausage and fresh cheeses. Pasta is plentiful and diverse, and the spit-roasted specialties are hard to resist.

AVERAGE DINNER FOR TWO: $40
DOES NOT INCLUDE WINE, TAX AND GRATUITY

RÔTI

155 STEUART STREET
SAN FRANCISCO, CA 94105
(415) 495-6500

Visa & Major Credit Cards
Dinner Daily • Lunch Mon-Fri

General Manager
PATRICK COLL

Executive Chef
PATRICIA TRACEY

Recommended Items

Appetizers
ONION SOUP • RED CURRY
MUSSELS • GINGER-CURED
SALMON • GRILLED FLATBREAD

Entrées
SPIT-ROASTED HALF CHICKEN
WITH LEMON & THYME
• SEARED SCALLOPS WITH
SPINACH & TOMATOES
• FILET MIGNON WITH
GREEN PEPPERCORN SAUCE
• BLACK & WHITE
CREME BRULÉE

RÔTI, IN THE HOTEL GRIFFON, IS A DYNAMIC GATHERING place for the downtown crowd. Guests enter a book-lined marble foyer, then pass through a cozy lobby with an elegant zinc bar. A rustic open rotisserie and country-style fireplace give way to a leather- and brass-appointed dining room with a gleaming open kitchen. This is followed by a mezzanine dining room with a spectacular view of the waterfront. ♦ In this warm, richly textured setting, Chef Tricia Tracey takes Rôti's West Coast American cuisine to glorious heights. Along with Executive Chef/Proprietor Cindy Pawlcyn, she combines Northern California produce, fresh local seafood, and spit-roasted fowl, meats and game in a hearty, American-style menu designed to suit varied tastes. Garlic mashed potatoes and seasoned onion rings are musts with any entrée. ♦ Rôti's Regional California wine list reflects a variety of wines from Napa, Sonoma and the Central Coast to complement your dining experience.

AVERAGE DINNER FOR TWO: $60
DOES NOT INCLUDE WINE, TAX AND GRATUITY

CONTEMPORARY FRENCH

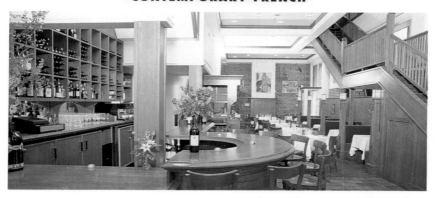

RUBICON

558 SACRAMENTO STREET
AT SANSOME
SAN FRANCISCO, CA 94111
(415) 434-4100

Visa & Major Credit Cards
Dinner Mon-Sat • Lunch Mon-Fri

Proprietor
DREW NIEPORENT

Executive Chef
TRACI DES JARDINS

Recommended Items

Appetizers
SEARED SCALLOPS WITH
TRUFFLE MASHED POTATOES
• CRISPY DUCK CONFIT
WITH CANNELINI BEAN
SALAD & FRISEE

Entrées
SEARED TUNA WITH CHICK
PEA PANCAKE & TOMATO
CONFIT • GRILLED BEEF
FILET WITH POTATO GRATIN,
PORTABELLOS & RED
WINE SAUCE

RUBICON EXUDES SUCCESS WITHOUT OSTENTATION. THE handsome bar and long bannister are constructed from a beautiful cherry wood, as are the cabinets throughout. Downstairs, brick walls and slate floors lend an old San Francisco flavor, while upstairs all is cozy and elegant. ♦ The restrained decor allows Chef Traci Des Jardins' creations to star. Traci's past training is impressive. She worked with the Troisgros family in France, at Patina in Los Angeles and earned her local stripes at Elka. Provencal in inspiration, her dishes are robust yet elegant, with unfussy presentations and masterful sauces. ♦ Rubicon has impeccable credentials. New York restaurateur Drew Nieporent (Montrachet, Tribeca Grill) heads the team, backed by Robert DeNiro, Francis Ford Coppola and Robin Williams. Behind the outstanding wine list is Master Sommelier Larry Stone. Add the irresistible desserts of Pastry Chef Elizabeth Falkner, and it's easy to see why Rubicon has earned the devotion of San Francisco's gourmet crowd.

AVERAGE DINNER FOR TWO: $80
DOES NOT INCLUDE WINE, TAX AND GRATUITY

VIP

STARS

150 REDWOOD ALLEY
OFF VAN NESS NEAR GOLDEN GATE
SAN FRANCISCO, CA 94102
(415) 861-7827
Visa & Major Credit Cards
Open Daily for Dinner • Lunch Mon-Fri

Proprietor/Executive Chef
JEREMIAH TOWER
Manager
FRANK F. REBUCAS

Chef
STEVEN C. VIRANIAN
Pastry Chef
EMILY LUCHETTI

Recommended Items

Appetizers
•ICED TUNA TARTARE WITH
LENTIL CHIPS, WASABI CREAM &
PEPPERED MANGOES • WILD
MUSHROOM TIMPALE WITH
ASPARAGUS & MARINATED
CHERRY TOMATOES

Entrées
•CRISPY SALMON
ON PESTO MASHERS WITH
MUSSELS & SAFFRON-FENNEL
BROTH • BRAISED BARON OF
LAMB SHANK WITH
ARTICHOKE RATATOUILLE,
CINNAMON-SCENTED
POLENTA & MINT

IF ONE PERSON COULD BE SINGLED OUT FOR REVOLUTIONIZING American cuisine, it would have to be Jeremiah Tower. As owner and executive chef of Stars since 1984, the Harvard-educated Tower has also redefined what makes a CA restaurant great: a seasonal menu of innovative dishes showcasing the freshest ingredients, a lively atmosphere as entertaining as it is welcoming, and a selective wine list of established winners and exciting newcomers. ◆ Today, Stars continues to reign as one of San Francisco's all time restaurant for all reasons. At night, the longest bar in the city hums with activity. A pianist entertains as diners enjoy a pre-or post-performance meal, a leisurely celebration with friends, or a late-night snack from the bar menu. Stars is also a favorite of socialites and power-lunchers. Its bistro-style decor, with every inch of wall space covered with vintage French posters or photos of Jeremiah and friends, appeal to everyone. ◆ Singled out for countless honors, Tower was recognized in 1993 as best regional chef in California by the prestigious James Beard Awards. The ever-changing menu at Stars is edible proof that this master will never rest on his laurels.

AVERAGE DINNER FOR TWO: $80
DOES NOT INCLUDE WINE, TAX AND GRATUITY

CONMEMORATIVO

100% natural gold tequila

Authentic. Aged in oak barrels. Naturally gold.
No caramel color. For over one hundred years.
Decidedly different. Uncommonly smooth.

SPLENDIDO

FOUR EMBARCADERO CENTER
PROMENADE LEVEL
SAN FRANCISCO, CA 94111
(415) 986-3222

Visa & Major Credit Cards
Dinner Sun-Sat • Lunch Mon-Fri

General Manager
TONY MONGELLO

Chef
CHRISTOPHER MAJER

Recommended Items

Appetizers
MEDITERRANEAN FISH &
SHELLFISH SOUP WITH ROUILLE
• CRAB & POTATO SALAD
WITH CITRUS VINAIGRETTE
• ASPARAGUS, ARTICHOKE &
HARICOT VERT SALAD

Entrées
GRILLED LAMB LOIN WITH
WHITE BEAN GARLIC FLAN,
FRIED SHALLOTS, TOMATO &
BASIL • PAN-ROASTED QUAIL
WITH FRIED ZUCCHINI,
LEMON & MINT • GRILLED
SWORDFISH WITH ROASTED
FENNEL & ORANGE

A SMASH HIT SINCE OPENING DAY, SPLENDIDO HAS AN INVITING, Mediterranean look thanks to noted restaurant designer Pat Kuleto. Several dining areas evoke a sixteenth century inn set somewhere on that warm sea's coast. Stone walls, pewter bar and a huge skylight framed with hand-hewn beams create a rustic environment that borrows from many Mediterranean countries. ♦ Chef Christopher Majer's menu is also inspired by those places, from Spain and Portugal to France and Italy. His light, health-conscious dishes take their cue from the seasons and also stress healthful oils rather than butter and cream. A former chef at New York's celebrated Quilted Giraffe and Arcadia, and San Francisco's Campton Place, Majer turns out plate-sized pizza variations from a wood-burning oven, using toppings such as goat cheese, marinated fennel and roasted tomato on a crunchy crust. Main courses range from grilled swordfish with lentil pancakes and pepper sauce to grilled veal chop with roasted garlic noodle cake. ♦ A heated patio overlooks the Ferry Building and a striking panorama of the Bay Bridge.

AVERAGE DINNER FOR TWO: $50
DOES NOT INCLUDE WINE, TAX AND GRATUITY

VIP

SILKS

MANDARIN ORIENTAL HOTEL
222 SANSOME STREET
SAN FRANCISCO, CA 94104
(415) 986-2020
Visa & Major Credit Cards
Breakfast, Lunch & Dinner Daily • Sunday Brunch

Manager
MARTIN KRAUS

Chef de Cuisine
KENNETH ORINGER

Recommended Items

Appetizers
SAMPLINGS OF THREE
TUNAS, TARTARE WITH LIME
& CAVIAR, SEARED NORI
WRAPPED & CRISPY SPRING
ROLL • TEMPURA OF JUMBO
SCALLOPS, BABY VEGETABLES
IN POTATO CAGE
Entrées
STRIPED BASS IN A GINGER
BOUILLON, THAI HERBS &
FRIED SHALLOTS • GRILLED
LAMB CHOPS WITH
INDONESIAN MARINADE
SHEPHERD'S PIE &
CHANTERELLE MUSHROOMS

SILKS TAKES THE MANDARIN ORIENTAL TRADITION TO A NEW level of comfort and accessibility, impressing guests with its casual elegance and high-caliber cuisine. The fresh new look of the dining room is created with warm colors, muted lighting and unique pieces of art that enhance the kitchen's contemporary and eclectic offerings. ♦ Chef de Cuisine Kenneth Oringer creates dishes that are an intriguing blend of the exotic and the familiar. His frequently changing dishes reflect a relentless commitment to seeking out the freshest ingredients available and serving them at their peak. Distinctive and creative, the two-, three- and four-course menus are the paragon of California dining with an Asian accent. And desserts, especially, are memorably presented. Try the chocolate cream sandwich with coffee candy or the passion fruit pudding cake with fresh strawberries and coconut sorbet.

AVERAGE DINNER FOR TWO: $75
DOES NOT INCLUDE WINE, TAX AND GRATUITY

CHINESE

TOMMY TOY'S
CUISINE CHINOISE

655 MONTGOMERY STREET
AT WASHINGTON
SAN FRANCISCO, CA 94108
(415) 397-4888

Visa & Major Credit Cards
Open Daily for Dinner • Lunch Mon-Fri

Proprietor
TOMMY TOY

Chef
HOWARD WONG

Recommended Items

Appetizers

PAN-FRIED FOIE GRAS WITH
SLICED PEAR & WATERCRESS IN
SWEET PICKLED GINGER SAUCE
• LOBSTER POTSTICKERS WITH
CHILI SAUCE

Entrées

WOK-CHARRED VEAL IN
SZECHUAN SAUCE • VANILLA
PRAWNS & RAISINS WITH FRESH
MELON • DUCKLING BREAST
SMOKED WITH CAMPHORWOOD
& TEA LEAVES, PLUM WINE
SAUCE

FIFTEEN YEARS AFTER HE OPENED THE HIGHLY SUCCESSFUL Imperial Palace, Tommy Toy did it again with Tommy Toy's. This time, he created a sumptuous restaurant off the beaten track, "for discriminating people who want an elegant French touch to their Chinese cuisine." In 1990, the restaurant was elected to the Restaurant Hall of Fame for excellence and innovation and is a perennial Mobil Four Star award winner. ♦ You won't find chopsticks here, only silverware, porcelain, authentic Chinese bridal lamps, and an incomparable display of Chinese ceramics and art from the private collection of Toy's partner, Joe Yuey. Toy, trained as an interior decorator, has recreated the opulence of the nineteenth-century Empress Dowager's reading room, with ancient "Powder Paintings" framed in sandalwood and hand-carved antique wood archways from mainland China. ♦ The food here is no less opulent, consisting of Cantonese and Szechuan dishes refined by Toy's own palate. Ask him to design your menu himself, and you will enjoy a most memorable meal.

AVERAGE DINNER FOR TWO: $70
DOES NOT INCLUDE WINE, TAX AND GRATUITY

VIP

VENTICELLO

1257 TAYLOR STREET
AT WASHINGTON
SAN FRANCISCO, CA 94108
(415) 922-2545

Visa & Major Credit Cards
Open Daily • Dinner Only

Proprietor
MICHAEL DEEB

Chef
DAVID BASTIDE

Recommended Items

Appetizers

• SLICED RAW ANGUS BEEF
ON ARUGULA W/SHAVED PARME-
SAN, CAPERS & LEMON
• GRILLED PRAWNS WRAPPED IN
PANCETTA W/ROASTED
BELL PEPPER SAUCE

Entrées

• RAVIOLI STUFFED W/
ROASTED PHEASANT W/
SAGE-INFUSED BUTTER
• ROSEMARY-CRUSTED AHI TUNA
SEARED & SERVED RARE
W/LEMON-CAPER BUTTER SAUCE
• VEAL SCALLOPINE SAUTÉED &
TOPPED W/WILD MUSHROOMS
& MARSALA WINE SAUCE

IN A NEIGHBORHOOD KNOWN FOR ITS CLASSY HOTELS AND expensive restaurants, Venticello is like a breath of fresh air. Hardly visible from the street, this cozy Italian eatery has the appeal of an old friend. Whether it's your first visit or your fortieth, you feel instantly embraced by the mellow ambiance and down-to-earth food. ♦ Venticello's dining room is small but high-ceilinged, with wood floors, country-style chairs and copper-and-ochre sponged walls. The walls are bare except for a tall, ornate wine cabinet, a wood-framed mirror, and an antique door, (its top being open to reveal yet another mirror). A blue ceramic oven sits inside a serving island, where open bottles of wine chill in a huge copper pot. Subdued lighting puts diners completely at ease. ♦ In this relaxed atmosphere, nothing could taste better than Chef David Bastide's fresh ravioli. A house specialty, it changes weekly, as does the rest of the small menu. Starters might include grilled shrimp wrapped in pancetta or a large plate of *antipasto* to share, and there is always a choice of at least five pastas. For dessert, it's hard to say no to the stellar *tiramisu*.

AVERAGE DINNER FOR TWO: $55
DOES NOT INCLUDE WINE, TAX AND GRATUITY

75

VERTIGO

600 MONTGOMERY STREET
AT CLAY
SAN FRANCISCO, CA 94111
(415) 433-7250

Visa & Major Credit Cards
Dinner Mon-Sat • Lunch Mon-Fri

Proprietors
DOUG WASHINGTON
NANCY MOOTZ

Chef
MARK LUSARDI

Recommended Items

Appetizers

PROVENCAL VEGETABLE SALAD
WITH GOAT CHEESE
PROFITEROLES • SMOKED
PHEASANT SALAD WITH APPLES,
ROQUEFORT & WALNUT OIL

Entrées

PORCINI SEARED SEABASS WITH
SCALLION RISOTTO CAKE AND
WILD MUSHROOM RAGOUT
• GINGER-LEMONGRASS ROAST
POUSSIN WITH TATSOI-SHIITAKE
SALAD, SWEET POTATO FRIES
• GRILLED BEEF FILET WITH
SWISS CHARD TORTE,
PORTOBELLOS, RED WINE SAUCE

SET IN THE BASE OF SAN FRANCISCO'S FAMOUS TRANSAMERICA pyramid building, Vertigo inspires nothing but comfort and pleasure. A Whispering fountain in the garden along the walkway sets a mellow mood, while inside, two levels of polished wood, copper-gold tones and spacious booths soften the drama of massive concrete beams and huge skylights. The lighting is done so masterfully that it creates an oasis of privacy for each table. ♦ This sophisticated yet warm setting is the work of two restaurant pros: Nancy Mootz, former vice-president of the Kimpton Group, who launched such famous restaurants as Kuleto's and Postrio, and Doug Washington, familiar to many as the friendly maître d'/manager of Square One, Postrio and Moose's. ♦ They launched Vertigo in February, 1995, with Chef Mark Lusardi in the kitchen. Tutored in New York by David Bouley (Bouley) and Thomas Colicchio (Mondrian), Lusardi honed his style, which he describes as "French technique and Italian soul with Japanese and Vietnamese influences," at Rubicon and Aqua. The bright flavors, intensified by vinaigrettes, herbs and natural jus, are as invigorating as the stunning decor.

AVERAGE DINNER FOR TWO: $65
DOES NOT INCLUDE WINE, TAX AND GRATUITY

CALIFORNIA/FRENCH

VICTOR'S

ST. FRANCIS HOTEL
335 POWELL STREET
SAN FRANCISCO, CA 94102
(415) 774-0253

Visa & Major Credit Cards
Open Daily for Dinner • Sunday Brunch

Director of Restaurants
BABETTE SHADE

Chef de Cuisine
FABRICE MARCON

Recommended Items

Appetizers
SONOMA FOIE GRAS WITH
FRESH PLUM & BLACK
PEPPERCORN • SMOKED FARM
RAISED SQUAB WITH CANDIED
KUMQUAT, GRILLED FENNEL
& PORT WINE SAUCE

Entrées
ROASTED CHILEAN SEA
BASS, CREAMY SPINACH &
PARMESAN FLAVORED
CRISPY POTATOES
• ROASTED LOBSTER,
ANGEL HAIR PASTA, WILD
MUSHROOMS & LOBSTER JUS

ON THE TOP FLOOR OF THE PRESTIGIOUS ST. FRANCIS HOTEL, the award-winning Victor's is a truly special find: a great hotel serving excellent food in a room with a spectacular view. After a breathtaking ride up thirty stories in an outside glass elevator, guests enter an elegant, wood-paneled corridor with recessed bookshelves housing leather-bound classics. In the dining room, floor-to-ceiling windows maximize the view of San Francisco and the Bay. ♦ Chef de Cuisine Fabrice Marcon, responding to the demands of his guests for Light French California cuisine, has redefined a series of traditional recipes incorporating light sauces made to order with fresh produce from the Bay Area. Dinner is enhanced by selections from a wine cellar that features more than 25,000 bottles. ♦ Sunday brunch at Victor's is a San Francisco tradition that draws a faithful local clientele.

AVERAGE DINNER FOR TWO: $80
DOES NOT INCLUDE WINE, TAX AND GRATUITY

VERY BISTRO...

EXOTIC. INTRIGUING. STYLISH. SOPHISTICATED.
TIA CAPPUCCINO. ICED OR HOT.

Tia Maria®

THE WORLD'S FINEST COFFEE LIQUEUR.

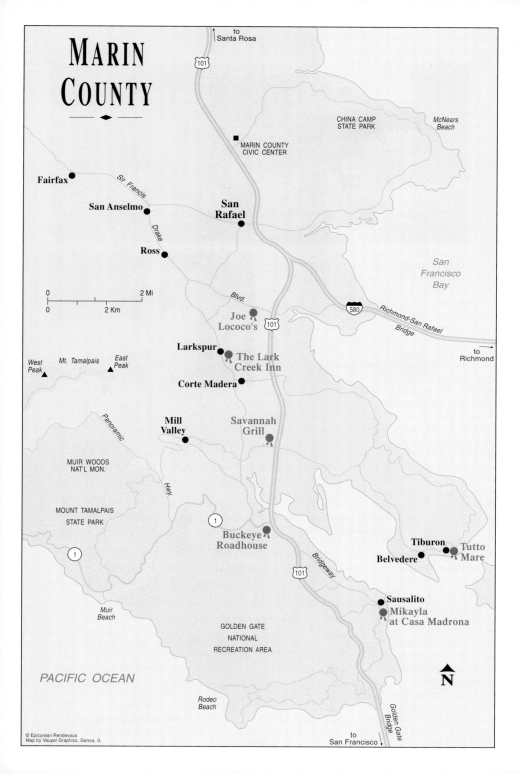

MARIN
COUNTY

to
Santa Rosa

101

MARIN COUNTY
CIVIC CENTER

CHINA CAMP
STATE PARK

McNears
Beach

Fairfax

Sir Francis

San Anselmo

Drake

San
Rafael

Ross

San
Francisco
Bay

0   2 Mi
0   2 Km

Blvd.

Joe
Lococo's

101

580

Richmond-San Rafael

Bridge

to
Richmond

West
Peak

Mt. Tamalpais

East
Peak

Larkspur

The Lark
Creek Inn

Corte Madera

Panoramic

MUIR WOODS
NAT'L MON.

Mill
Valley

Savannah
Grill

Hwy.

MOUNT TAMALPAIS

STATE PARK

1

1

Buckeye
Roadhouse

Bridgeway

Tiburon

Belvedere

Tutto
Mare

101

Muir
Beach

Sausalito

Mikayla
at Casa Madrona

GOLDEN GATE

NATIONAL

RECREATION AREA

PACIFIC OCEAN

N

Rodeo
Beach

Golden Gate
Bridge

to
San Francisco

© Epicurean Rendevous
Map by Vaupel Graphics, Genoa, IL

BUCKEYE ROADHOUSE

15 SHORELINE HIGHWAY
MILL VALLEY, CA 94941
(415) 331-2600

Visa & MasterCard
Open Daily • Lunch & Dinner • Sunday Brunch

General Manager
PATRICK COLL

Chef
JOHN C. BEARDSLEY

Recommended Items

Appetizers

HOUSEMADE SOUP DAILY

• ONION RINGS WITH
HOUSEMADE KETCHUP

• HOUSE-SMOKED
ATLANTIC SALMON WITH
POTATO LEEK PANCAKE

Entrées

PEPPER & LEMON
CREOLE SHRIMP WITH
GARLIC MASHED POTATOES

• MARINATED CHICKEN BREAST
WITH ROASTED PEPPERS &
GRILLED BUTTERNUT SQUASH

• DRY AGED NEW YORK
STEAK WITH OR WITHOUT
CHICKASAW COUNTY GLAZE

DOTTING THE AMERICAN LANDSCAPE FROM ROUTE 66 TO Highway 95, roadhouses are eateries that become temporary homes to those on the road, memorized by locals and strangers passing. ♦ Buckeye Roadhouse, named for the trees in its backyard, has perched on busy Shoreline Highway since 1937. Bill Higgins used to drive by it everyday, but now he's inside looking out having turned Buckeye into his version of what a Marin roadhouse should be. He kept the robust lodge-look of the original with its great river rock fireplace, inlaid beams and stair rails made of braided Golden Gate Bridge cable, adding Italian chandeliers, sconces and other touches. Then in the process of discovering roadhouse cuisine, he and partner Bill Upson managed to redefine it. ♦ What is it? In this case: American, Bay Area style. Imagine a meal served in an Edward Hopper painting. Then picture Cindy Pawlcyn in the kitchen making sure only the finest, freshest ingredients from local purveyors make it into her pots and pans and you'll get the idea. The food is fun and the place a haven for a quick lunch, deluxe dinner, or cocktails in the refined sports bar.

AVERAGE DINNER FOR TWO: $50
DOES NOT INCLUDE WINE, TAX AND GRATUITY

JOE LoCoco's

300 DRAKES LANDING ROAD
AT SIR FRANCIS DRAKE
GREENBRAE, CA 94904
(415) 925-0808

Visa & Major Credit Cards
Open Daily for Dinner • Lunch Mon-Fri

Chef/Proprietor
JOE LoCOCO

Chef
MARCO FIORINI

Recommended Items

Appetizers
MOZZARELLA GRILLED ON
SKEWERS ROMAN-STYLE
• GRILLED TUSCAN BREAD
WITH WILD MUSHROOMS &
FRESH HERBS • ANTIPASTI BAR

Entrées
RISOTTO WITH QUAIL &
BLUEBERRIES • GRILLED MAINE
LOBSTER WITH CHAMPAGNE
RISOTTO • SPAGHETTI
WITH ROASTED ROMAN
TOMATOES & FRESH HERBS

YOU KNOW YOU'RE ON TO SOMETHING GOOD WHEN YOU LEAVE A restaurant to open another and the entire clientele follows *en masse.* Joe LoCoco is the lucky man blessed with such an appreciative following. Due to its unpretentious ambiance and LoCoco's considerable talents, the restaurant has been a success since its opening in 1987. ♦ LoCoco, raised in Buffalo, spent time in Livorno, Italy, honing his skills in preparing traditional Italian cuisine. He and Chef Marco Fiorini use age-old recipes (some dating from medieval times) utilizing fresh vegetables, housemade pasta and wild game to create hearty, peasant-style dishes. ♦ The dining room's peach stucco walls are covered with plates from Siena, paintings from Florence and Tuscan pottery. Large windows open on views of the Bay and Mt. Tamalpais. Dining *al fresco* on the outdoor patio is another way to savor the Tuscan experience.

AVERAGE DINNER FOR TWO: $45
DOES NOT INCLUDE WINE, TAX AND GRATUITY

81

THE LARK CREEK INN

234 MAGNOLIA AVENUE
LARKSPUR, CA 94939
(415) 924-7766

Visa & Major Credit Cards
Open Daily for Dinner • Lunch Mon-Fri
Sunday Brunch

Chef/Owner
BRADLEY OGDEN
Owner
MICHAEL DELLAR

Manager
RON P. VALE
Chef
JULES PAULK

Recommended Items

Appetizers
ONION FLATBREAD WITH
TOMATOES, EGGPLANT,
DRY-AGED JACK CHEESE &
OLIVE PESTO • SUMMER
VEGETABLE STEW
WITH LOBSTER &
HOMEMADE EGG NOODLES

Entrées
OVEN-ROASTED SALMON
WITH CORN SPOONBREAD,
BARBECUED PRAWNS &
CHERVIL TOMATO BROTH
• ROTISSERIE OF QUAIL
WITH GRILLED LEEKS &
TRUFFLE MASHED POTATOES

LIKE AN OLD-FASHIONED NEW ENGLAND COUNTRY RESTAURANT, The Lark Creek Inn has a timeless quality that resists trends and invites relaxation. Bradley Ogden, the James Beard Society Award winning chef who has given a new luster to American cuisine, and restaurateur Michael Dellar have put their talents together in what may be the most refreshing restaurant to open in years. ♦ "We are striving to have the kind of place where out-of-towners reserve in advance and locals drop by for lunch or dinner on a regular basis," says Dellar. White walls, hardwood floors, a creekside dining patio and a bar with its own menu characterize the setting for Bradley Ogden's robustly flavored yet simple cuisine. ♦ Ogden makes everything from scratch, from breads to jams and pickles. The award-winning all-American wine list is equally focused with over 200 selections. Brunch at The Lark Creek Inn may be the ultimate experience: apple-smoked ham steak with figs and melon, and wild berry flapjacks with Meyer lemon butter are but two of its many temptations.

AVERAGE DINNER FOR TWO: $60
DOES NOT INCLUDE WINE, TAX AND GRATUITY

AMERICAN

MIKAYLA
AT CASA MADRONA

801 BRIDGEWAY
SAUSALITO, CA 94965
(415) 331-5888

Visa & Major Credit Cards
Dinner Daily • Sunday Brunch

Proprietor
JOHN W. MAYS

Executive Chef
JOHN D. STATE
Sous Chef
DAVID M. LUTZ

Recommended Items

Appetizers

HOUSE-SMOKED SALMON WITH
CELERY ROOT REMOULADE
• GRILLED QUAIL WITH
ROASTED BEETS &
HORSERADISH DRESSING

Entrées

CHARRED PRIME SIRLOIN
WITH SALSIFY, ROASTED
POTATOES & SAUCE FOYOT
• POTATO-WRAPPED STRIPED
BASS WITH LEEK FONDUE &
RED WINE JUS • ROASTED
RACK OF LAMB WITH
COUSCOUS PROVENÇAL &
RED PEPPER JUS

SITTING IN MIKAYLA'S HIGH ABOVE THE SAUSALITO HARBOR, YOU feel as if you're floating on a cloud. Glass walls let nature do the painting, with uninterrupted vistas of water and white sails framed by wooded hills and the distant lights of the Bay Bridge. Such views could easily over-shadow the decor - unless the designer happens to be Laurel Burch. ♦ The internationally known artist and Sausalito resident has given the restau-rant her whimsical stamp, beginning with a stunning mural dedicated to Mikayla, Owner John Mays's daughter and the inspiration for the restau-rant's new name. Laurel's mythical images and vibrant colors continue throughout, and play on every surface, from chairbacks and candelabra to massive bas relief sculptures. ♦ Along with its new identity, Casa Madrona's famous restaurant has an outstanding new chef. He is John State, former sous chef of Bradley Ogden at the Lark Creek Inn. A master of sauces and reductions, State is a stickler for quality ingredients and invigorating flavors. His dishes are uncomplicated enough to enjoy every day, yet perfect for the most special occasion.

AVERAGE DINNER FOR TWO: $55
DOES NOT INCLUDE WINE, TAX AND GRATUITY

AMERICAN

SAVANNAH GRILL

55 TAMAL VISTA
AT MADERA
CORTE MADERA, CA 94925
(415) 924-6774

Visa & Major Credit Cards
Open Daily • Lunch & Dinner

Proprietor
KEITH JONES

Chef
JEFF ROSEN

Recommended items

Appetizers
CHICKEN SKEWER WITH
RED SESAME SALSA &
GRILLED SCALLIONS • GULF
PRAWNS WITH SPICY RED
CURRY CREAM, PEANUTS &
PAPAYA

Entrées
GARLIC FETTUCCINE WITH
PRAWNS, BAY SCALLOPS,
ROMA TOMATOES, ROASTED
GARLIC & AGED REGGIANO
CHEESE • SKIRT STEAK
MARINATED IN BLACK BEAN
CHILI SAUCE & BEER

IN MARIN, THE SAVANNAH GRILL IS THE PLACE TO SEE AND BE SEEN. With a cherrywood-and-brass decor created by designer Pat Kuleto, the restaurant is made for people-watching, with a long, narrow dining room overlooking a lively bar on one side and an attractive black-hooded open kitchen on the other. ♦ In this upbeat, unpretentious environment, Executive Chef Jeff Rosen concentrates on deftly prepared hardwood-grilled and smoked meats and seafood, and pasta specialties, with up to fifteen daily specials. The new, lighter menu follows the nutritional guidelines of the American Heart Association. ♦ Savannah Grill's fresh ingredients and Asian, Latin and European influences draw praise from food critics. "For a moderate price," writes *San Francisco Chronicle* critic Patricia Unterman, "they serve out of the ordinary, tasty food and treat everyone nicely."

AVERAGE DINNER FOR TWO: $40
DOES NOT INCLUDE WINE, TAX AND GRATUITY

TUTTO MARE

RISTORANTE E TAVERNA.

9 MAIN ST.
TIBURON, CA 94929
(415) 435-4747
Visa & Major Credit Cards
Open Daily • Lunch & Dinner • Sunday Brunch

General Managers
A.J. GILBERT
TONINO DROVANDI

Chef
JOE JACK

Recommended Items

Appetizers
SHAVED BABY ARTICHOKES &
FENNEL, LEMON, PARSLEY, MINT
• TUNA CARPACCIO, ARUGULA,
HORSERADISH • CARPACCIO:
DRY-AGED BEEF, CAPERS, REG-
GIANO, EXTRA VIRGIN OLIVE OIL

Entrées
SEA BASS-STUFFED MEZZELUNE,
GRILLED MONKFISH WRAPPED
IN PANCETTA STUFFED W/FIGS,
RAISINS, ESCAROLE, CANNELLINI
BEANS • RAINBOW TROUT
BAKED W/SPECK, POTATOES,
WILD MUSHROOMS

TUTTO MARE MEANS "EVERYTHING FROM THE SEA" IN ITALIAN, and this restaurant on Tiburon's panoramic waterfront lives up to its name. Downstairs is a lively, inexpensive *Taverna*, where diners can drop in for fresh oysters and shellfish, pizzas and salads, or enjoy a drink at the bar or by the fireplace. Upstairs is the *Ristorante*, with a wider choice of fare that includes housemade pastas, wood-grilled meats and fowl, and seafood specialties from Italy's coastal provinces. ♦ Both spaces boast huge exhibition kitchens, with galvanized steel counters and ceramic tile murals, and use muted tones of sage and lemon to create a soothing atmosphere. Oars hang from the *Ristorante's* ceiling, and glass doors open to the deck, where diners can watch the ferries dock as they sip a "fishbowl martini" or a glass of wine. ♦ Chef Joe Jack's unique menu recreates authentic Italian dishes seldom found in California. He often juxtaposes sweet savory flavors with fish and shellfish. His pastas are just as daring: the tortellini, for instance, are flavored with cocoa, filled with duck, and bathed in a sublime orange-sage butter.

AVERAGE DINNER FOR TWO: $50
DOES NOT INCLUDE WINE, TAX AND GRATUITY

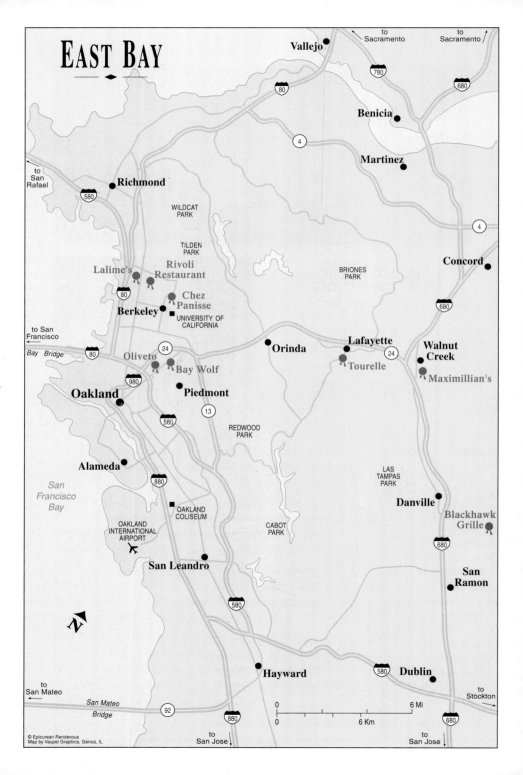

EAST BAY

Vallejo

to Sacramento

to Sacramento

780

80

Benicia

4

Martinez

to San Rafael

Richmond

580

4

WILDCAT PARK

TILDEN PARK

BRIONES PARK

Concord

680

Lalime's

Rivoli Restaurant

Chez Panisse

Berkeley

UNIVERSITY OF CALIFORNIA

80

Orinda

Lafayette

24

Walnut Creek

Maximillian's

Tourelle

to San Francisco

Bay Bridge

80

Oliveto

24

Bay Wolf

980

Oakland

Piedmont

13

REDWOOD PARK

LAS TAMPAS PARK

Danville

580

Blackhawk Grille

680

Alameda

San Francisco Bay

880

OAKLAND COLISEUM

CABOT PARK

San Ramon

OAKLAND INTERNATIONAL AIRPORT

San Leandro

580

to San Mateo

Hayward

580

Dublin

to Stockton

San Mateo Bridge

92

880

0   6 Mi

0   6 Km

680

© Epicurean Rendevous
Map by Vaupel Graphics, Genoa, IL

to San Jose

to San Jose

BAY WOLF

3853 PIEDMONT AVENUE
AT RIO VISTA
OAKLAND, CA 94611
(510) 655-6004

Visa & MasterCard Only
Open Daily for Dinner • Lunch Mon-Fri

Proprietor
LARRY GOLDMAN
Maître d'
MARK MCLEOD

Chef/Proprietor
MICHAEL WILD
Executive Chef
JOE NOUHAN

Recommended Items

Appetizers

WARM BUCKWHEAT CRÊPES
FILLED WITH FONTINA CHEESE,
PROSCIUTTO & SAGE
• "PANZANELLA"—ITALIAN-
STYLE BREAD SALAD WITH
MUSHROOMS, CUCUMBERS,
ARUGULA & GOAT CHEESE

Entrées

GRILLED SEA BASS WITH
GAZPACHO RELISH, NEW POTA-
TOES & TOMATO VINAIGRETTE
• DUCK WITH CHERRIES &
POTATO-CELERY ROOT PANCAKE
• BRAISED LAMB SHANKS WITH
WHITE BEANS & ROSEMARY

IT IS REASSURING TO KNOW THAT SINCERE RESTAURANTS ARE still doing well in this inconstant world. Oakland diners have depended upon Michael Wild and Larry Goldman to keep one step ahead of culinary fads ever since they took a vacant house and transformed it into the sunny, art-filled oasis that is the Bay Wolf today. ♦ Everything here feels comfortable, everything is just how it should be – the awning-covered deck, the gleaming brass espresso machine on the bar, and the friendly faces of the experienced waiters and waitresses. ♦ Lunch or dinner, Bay Wolf continues to delight and satisfy with its innovative and changing menus. Says Michael Wild, "After eighteen years it is still a joy to keep the food exciting." The restaurant's modest but formidable wine list has become legendary in the wine world.

AVERAGE DINNER FOR TWO: $50
DOES NOT INCLUDE WINE, TAX AND GRATUITY

BLACKHAWK GRILLE

BLACKHAWK PLAZA
DANVILLE, CA 94506
(510) 736-4295

Visa & Major Credit Cards
Open Daily for Dinner • Lunch Mon-Sat • Sunday Brunch

General Manager
TODD OHANIAN

Chef
ANNE MARIE
CASTIGLIONE

Recommended Items

Appetizers

BEEF CARPACCIO PILLOW, WILD
MUSHROOM AIOLI, ROASTED RED
POTATO, FETA & HERBS • SWEET
CORN FRITTERS, SMOKED DUCK,
ARUGULA & WALNUT SALAD,
RED PEPPER COULIS

Entrées

GRILLED FREE-RANGE
CHICKEN, CHANTERELLES,
WALLA WALLA ONIONS, ENGLISH
PEAS, FOUR-CHEESE RISOTTO
• GRILLED LAMB LOIN, POTATO &
BLACK OLIVE TERRINE, BRAISED
LEEKS, RED PEPPER OIL &
MUSTARD-THYME GLACE

GUESTS ENTERING BLACKHAWK GRILLE ARE IMMEDIATELY struck by the restaurant's unusual interior, particularly the mint-condition classic automobile displayed in the dining room. The car, along with sleek brushed steel accents and "hubcap" sconces, toasts nearby Behring Auto Museum. The roomy restaurant is the heart of Blackhawk Plaza, a cultural/retail complex and water park. Towering windows and "waterfront" patio give diners an unobstructed view of sparkling streams and dramatic waterfalls. ♦ An open kitchen offers Mediterranean-style, seasonal fare. Dishes range from nature-fed meat, poultry, game and seafood to pasta and pizza. Notes Chef Anne Marie Castiglione, "Although I concentrate on combining rustic foods to produce an array of dishes that meets my primary goal of satisfying the diner, I take particular delight in introducing a guest to something new." A selection of premium wines by-the-glass is offered from the 3,000-bottle wine cellar which doubles as a banquet room.

AVERAGE DINNER FOR TWO: $55
DOES NOT INCLUDE WINE, TAX AND GRATUITY

LALIME'S

1329 GILMAN STREET
AT NIELSON
BERKELEY, CA 94706
(510) 527-9838
Visa & Major Credit Cards
Open Daily for Dinner

Chef/Proprietor
HAIG KRIKORIAN
Proprietor
CYNTHIA LALIME KRIKORIAN

Chef de Cuisine
FRANCES WILSON

Recommended Items

Appetizers
MUSSEL, SAFFRON & PERNOD
SOUP • SWEETBREADS SAUTÉED
IN A BEAUMES-DE-VENISE SAUCE
• LINGUINE WITH SMOKED
TROUT, CAPERS & RED ONIONS

Entrées
GRILLED JUNIPER BERRY-CURED
PORK CHOP, WITH GRATIN OF
YAMS, MUSHROOMS & RED
BELL PEPPERS • CRACKED
PEPPER-CRUSTED SALMON
COOKED ON THE IRON &
SERVED WITH SAUTÉED CORN

LALIME'S HAS THE HEART OF A NEIGHBORHOOD EATERY AND THE soul of a first-class restaurant. It is filled with a lively crowd that looks very comfortable in the homey two-tiered dining room. The unpretentious windowboxes overflowing with flowers and rag rugs on the banquettes give no hint of the sophisticated flavors explored by Chef Haig Krikorian. ♦ Every night, regulars from all around the Bay Area, alerted by Proprietor Cynthia Lalime Krikorian's monthly newsletter, make the trek to Gilman Street to feast on Lalime's renowned daily prix-fixe dinner and à la carte selections. One night the menu could be a rich lobster and smoked salmon chowder, a thin strip of zucchini enclosed grilled scallops atop a sweet acorn squash purée, or a roast duck glazed with Port wine and demi-glace on a bed of creamy polenta. ♦ Sometimes Chef Haig draws on his Armenian background, or he and Chef de Cuisine Frances Wilson let their imaginations fly around the world for inspiration. What never changes is the cuisine's consistent excellence, which explains why Lalime's was named among the top twelve Bay Area restaurants by the prestigious French *Gault-Millau*.

AVERAGE DINNER FOR TWO: $50
DOES NOT INCLUDE WINE, TAX AND GRATUITY

CHEZ PANISSE

1517 SHATTUCK AVENUE
AT CEDAR
BERKELEY, CA 94709
(510) 548-5525

Visa & Major Credit Cards
Closed Sunday • Dinner Only

Chef/Proprietor
ALICE WATERS

Pastry Chef
LINDSEY SHERE

Recommended Items

Appetizers
FRESH FIG & ONION
SALAD WITH
GARDEN LETTUCE &
BALSAMIC VINEGAR

Entrées
• BAKED FISH
WITH YELLOW
TOMATOES & GREEN
OLIVES • GRILLED
WHEELER RANCH
PORK WITH CORN &
CHANTERELLE RISOTTO

FAMED FOR ORIGINALITY, THE UNCOMPROMISING QUALITY OF ITS ingredients and the vision of Alice Waters, Chez Panisse is a great American restaurant with an international reputation. ♦ The free spirit so pervasive in Berkeley also prevails in this kitchen. Since opening in 1971, Chez Panisse has seldom repeated a dish on its prix-fixe menu (currently $35 Monday; $55 Tuesday, Wednesday, Thursday; $65 weekends). As the culinary shrine of the American food revolution, it has fresh produce suppliers knocking on the back door every day. Their produce is organically grown and their meat contains no chemicals. "We're never satisfied," Waters says. "We're always reaching and searching, searching and reaching." Pastry Chef Lindsey Shere is well reknowed for her exquisite dessert creations. ♦ Other culinary heavyweights have cooked here, then gone on to create their own noted kitchens – Jeremiah Tower and Joyce Goldstein, to name a few.

AVERAGE DINNER FOR TWO: $100-200
DOES NOT INCLUDE WINE, TAX AND GRATUITY

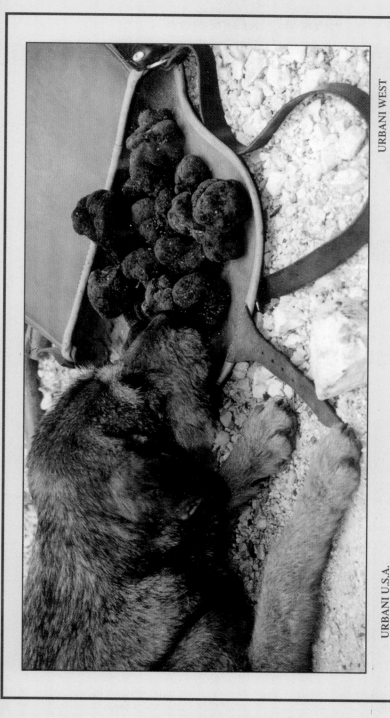

FRENCH CALIFORNIA

MAXIMILLIAN'S

1604 LOCUST STREET
NEAR BONANZA
WALNUT CREEK, CA 94596
(510) 932-1474

Visa & Major Credit Cards
Closed Sunday • Lunch & Dinner

Proprietor
MAX WOLFE

Chef
CHRISTIAN MÜLLER
Sous Chef
ANTHONY NATALI PHIE

Recommended Items

Appetizers
MARINATED SCALLOPS
W/PAPAYA SALSA & CHIPOTLE
CREAM • COCONUT-CRUSTED
PRAWNS W/PINEAPPLE CHUTNEY,
JASMINE RICE & CURRY YOGURT

Entrées
APPLE CIDER MARINATED PORK
TENDERLOIN W/SWEET POTATO
PANCAKES & JALAPEÑO-
MUSTARD GLAZE
• FENNEL SEED & BLACK
PEPPER CRUSTED FILET OF
KING SALMON W/APPLEWOOD
SMOKED LEEK SAUCE

MAXIMILLIAN'S HAS BEEN ONE OF THE EAST BAY'S PREMIER dining establishments for eighteen years. The street level dining room has a warm, comfortable and upscale feel - perfect for the business lunch. The upstairs dining room has more traditional ambiance with old brick and oak touches. Service is formal in this intimate, romantic setting. ♦ Live Jazz is featured Thursday through Saturday evenings in the lounge. Maximillian's downtown location and proximity to the Regional Center for the Arts draws local crowds as well as theatre patrons looking for an evening of fun and entertainment. ♦ In keeping with the restaurant's far-reaching culinary inspirations, Chef Christian Müller creates savory dishes which combines the influence of California, Europe and Asia. His stylish cuisine is not only pleasing to the palate, but to the eyes as well.

AVERAGE DINNER FOR TWO: $40
DOES NOT INCLUDE WINE, TAX AND GRATUITY

OLIVETO

5655 COLLEGE AVENUE
NEAR BART STATION
OAKLAND, CA 94618
(510) 547-5356

Visa & Major Credit Cards
Open Daily for Dinner • Lunch Mon–Fri

Proprietor	*Chef*
MAGGIE BLYTH KLEIN	PAUL BERTOLLI

Recommended Items

Appetizers

WARM WILD MUSHROOM SALAD
• GNOCCHI WITH ASPARAGUS
& PROSCIUTTO • FETTUCCINE
WITH SQUID, GARLIC & PARSLEY

Entrées

CHICKEN SALTIMBOCCA
• 6-HOUR SHOULDER OF LAMB
• NORTHERN HALIBUT
AL'AGRUMATO

IN THE SPRING OF 1995, LONGTIME FRIEND OF OLIVETO, PAUL Bertolli, joined Owner Maggie Klein to become Chef and Partner. ♦ Having spent a year cooking in Italy, and being a frequent visitor there, he brought with him not only his appreciation for the freshest locally grown seasonal ingredients, but also an understanding of the robust flavor that defines Northern Italian cooking. ♦ In a bright, airy second-floor dining room that feels like an Italian *casa colonica*, Chef Paul serves such items as homemade cured salame, wild fennel fritters, ravioli of ricotta and five herbs, swordfish involtini, veal chops salsa verde and lamb Scottadito. Oliveto's luscious dessert menu includes tarts and cakes redolent with seasonal fruits. The rich warm chocolate soufflé cake is eminently satisfying all year long.

AVERAGE DINNER FOR TWO: $50
DOES NOT INCLUDE WINE, TAX AND GRATUITY

VIP

RIVOLI

1539 SOLANO AVE.
AT NIELSON
BERKELEY, CA 94707
(510) 526-2542
Visa & Major Credit Cards
Open Daily for Dinner

Proprietor
ROSCOE SKIPPER

Chef/Proprietor
WENDY BRUCKER

Recommended Items

Appetizers

PORTOBELLO MUSHROOM FRIT-
TERS W/PARMESAN, CAPERS,
ARUGULA & LEMON AIOLI
• PROSCIUTTO NAPOLEON
W/CELERY ROOT, TRUFFLE OIL,
SWEET & SOUR CARROTS

Entrées

ROAST SUGAR PUMPKIN & SAGE
RISOTTO W/PEARL ONIONS,
GREENS & PARMESAN • GRILLED
HALIBUT W/CORN &
CHANTRELLE RAGOUT &
MASHED POTATOES • ROAST
RACK OF LAMB W/POMEGRANATE
JUS & WILD RICE & POTATO
GRATIN

WHAT HAPPENS WHEN TWO YOUNG RESTAURANT PROS FROM SAN Francisco marry and move to Berkeley? If they are Wendy Brucker and Roscoe Skipper, they open Rivoli to instant applause. She is the talented chef, a graduate of the California Culinary Academy who perfected her skills at Ernie's Square One and Stars. He is the friendly host, an English-lit major and mastermind of an interesting, affordable wine list, who worked as a waiter/bartender at Masa's, Square One and Bizou. They met at Square One, honeymooned in Paris near the Rue de Rivoli, and the rest is history. ◆ Opened in 1994, Rivoli's Mediterranean-influenced cuisine has already earned high praise from *Gourmet*, the *San Francisco Chronicle* and many other publications. The decor is cheery: yellow bricks meet bold red cabinets, paintings of food and flowers abound, and a glass wall frames a lovely garden of magnolias, camelias, impatiens and ferns. ◆ Just as upbeat is Chef Brucker's style, which harmonizes spontaneity, simplicity and the freshest available local ingredients. Her portobello mushroom fritters are a must, and if you're lucky, the weekly menu will include warm buckweat crêpes with Meyer lemon mascarpone and berry sauce.

AVERAGE DINNER FOR TWO: $50
DOES NOT INCLUDE WINE, TAX AND GRATUITY

TOURELLE

3565 MT. DIABLO BOULEVARD
AT OAK HILL
LAFAYETTE, CA 94549
(510) 284-3565
Visa & Major Credit Cards
Open Daily • Lunch & Dinner • Sunday Brunch

Manager
LANCE BELLAMY

Chef
STEPHEN SILVA

Recommended Items

♦

Appetizers

WARM GOAT CHEESE & GRILLED EGGPLANT, MIXED GREENS, NICOISE OLIVES & SUN DRIED TOMATO • CREAMY POLENTA , WILD MUSHROOMS & MASCARPONE CHEESE • CRISPY CURRIED CRAB CAKE, CUCUMBERS & BASIL

Entrées

WILD MUSHROOM RISOTTO WHITE TRUFFLE OIL & CHIVES • GRILLED LOIN OF LAMB, ROAST GARLIC NOODLE CAKE, TOMATO, EGGPLANT & BASIL • GRILLED SALMON LEMON MASHED POTATOES, HAZELNUTS & LOBSTER CREAM

TAKE A WALK DOWN A FLAGSTONE PATH PAST FRAGRANT HERB and flower gardens and be transported to the South of France. Tourelle, a beautiful and historic vine-covered chateau is truly authentic. It still retains the original brick tower from which Tourelle ("little tower") gets its name. ♦ One of the most romantic restaurants in the Bay Area, Tourelle has a timeless, European ambiance. The high vaulted ceilings, pine floors and clean-lined furniture are reminiscent of a Mediterranean villa, an ideal backdrop for Chef Stephen Silva's contemporary Mediterranean cuisine. A graduate of the Culinary Institute of America in Hyde Park, New York, he blends Italian and French flavors in direct, uncomplicated dishes. ♦ The lively exhibition kitchen, redesigned by Pat Kuleto, is visible from all dining rooms. Outdoor garden dining is available in season.

AVERAGE DINNER FOR TWO: $50
DOES NOT INCLUDE WINE, TAX AND GRATUITY

Authentic Irish Stout. Traditionally Brewed in Cork, Ireland Since 1856.
Also available in Draft Fresh cans.

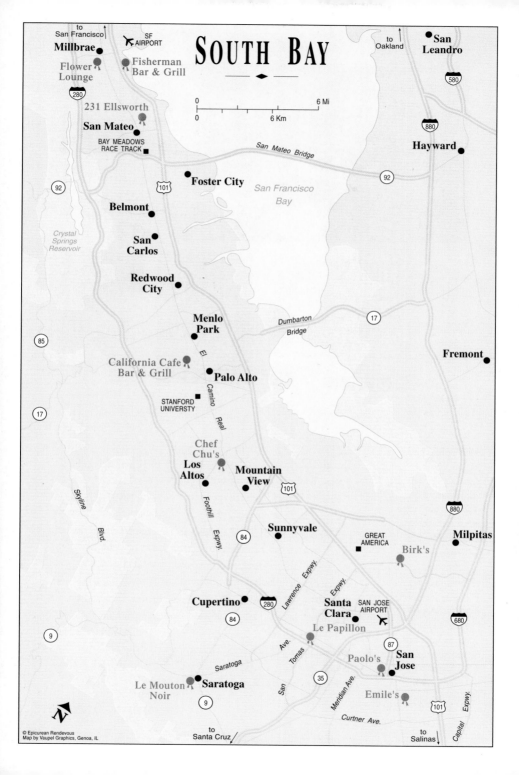

SOUTH BAY

to
San Francisco

SF
AIRPORT

Millbrae

Flower Lounge

Fisherman Bar & Grill

280

231 Ellsworth

San Mateo

BAY MEADOWS
RACE TRACK

San Mateo Bridge

101

Foster City

San Francisco
Bay

92

Belmont

92

Crystal
Springs
Reservoir

San Carlos

Redwood City

Menlo Park

Dumbarton
Bridge

17

85

El Camino Real

California Cafe Bar & Grill

Palo Alto

STANFORD
UNIVERSTY

17

Chef Chu's

Los Altos

Mountain View

101

Foothill Expwy.

Skyline

Blvd.

84

Sunnyvale

GREAT
AMERICA

Birk's

880

Milpitas

9

Cupertino

280

84

Lawrence Expwy.

Expwy.

Santa Clara

SAN JOSE
AIRPORT

Le Papillon

Paolo's

87

San Jose

680

Ave.

Tomas

35

Meridian Ave.

Le Mouton Noir

Saratoga

Saratoga

San

9

Emile's

101

Capital Expwy.

to
San Francisco

to
Oakland

San Leandro

580

880

Hayward

Fremont

Curtner Ave.

to
Santa Cruz

to
Salinas

0   6 Mi
0   6 Km

N

BIRK'S

3955 FREEDOM CIRCLE
AT HWY. 101 & GREAT AMERICA PKWY.
SANTA CLARA, CA 95054
(408) 980-6400

Visa & Major Credit Cards
Open Daily for Dinner • Lunch Mon-Fri

Proprietors
JIM SCHLOSS
DON DURANTE

Executive Chef
JEFF EDELMAN
Sous Chef
ARTHUR L. FEASEL

Recommended Items

Appetizers
CRISP FRIED CALAMARI
• CAJUN POPCORN SHRIMP
• BEEF CARPACCIO WITH
MUSTARD SAUCE &
FRIED CAPERS
Entrées
PEPPER FILET WITH
COGNAC & GREEN
PEPPERCORN SAUCE
• MIXED GRILL OF
CHICKEN, LAMB CHOP,
FILET MIGNON, CRAB CAKE
• INDIAN SALMON BAKED
IN HERB CRUST

A JOINT EFFORT BY BIRK McCANDLESS, JIM SCHLOSS AND DON Durante, Birk's is a sophisticated American grill designed by Pat Kuleto. Lodged in a futuristic building beneath the first of two proposed McCandless Towers, it is the place where the Silicon Valley comes to unwind. ◆ A long mahogany bar faces the entrance, with three brass standards that dispense eighteen draft beers. Behind the bar, open shelves loaded with premium spirits reach to a redwood-beamed ceiling. Multilevel dining areas provide a choice of deep booths and private tables or counter seating by an open-to-view kitchen. ◆ "We do food America loves and people will come back to," says Jim Schloss. Conceived by Durante, owner of Le Mouton Noir in Saratoga, the traditional menu of grilled and smoked meat, fish and fowl is brought to life by Jeff Edelman, who honed his skills at California Café in Palo Alto and other prestigious Bay Area kitchens.

AVERAGE DINNER FOR TWO: $60
DOES NOT INCLUDE WINE, TAX AND GRATUITY

CALIFORNIA CAFÉ

700 WELCH RD.
IN THE STANFORD BARN
PALO ALTO, CA 94304
(415) 325-2233
Visa & Major Credit Cards
Open Daily • Lunch & Dinner • Sunday Brunch

General Manager
MAX BORINSTEIN

Executive Chef
MARK STARK

Recommended Items

Appetizers

ARTICHOKE & PORTOBELLO MUSHROOM FRITTERS, CURRY AIOLI, FRESH TOMATO CHUTNEY • ROASTED VEGETABLE TERRINE, FETA, CUCUMBER & PEPPER SALAD

Entrées

BEET & CHEVRE RAVIOLI, GRILLED PORTOBELLO MUSH-ROOMS, ROSEMARY, WILTED GREENS • MUSCOVY DUCK, ASPARAGUS, CHICKPEA-LENTIL PANCAKES, GOLDEN TURNIPS, PRESERVED PLUMS • SEARED AHI TUNA, BRAISED SHIITAKE MUSH-ROOMS, EGGPLANT, GREEN HERB DUMPLINGS, MISO VINAIGRETTE

ON A BEAUTIFUL SPRING DAY AT THE CALIFORNIA CAFÉ, A WOMAN was overheard saying to her companion, "I love this place. Here, every-one can be happy." She was referring to the variety on the menu, but she might just as well have been talking about the ambiance or the ser-vice, for the California Café aims to please and succeeds. ♦ For lunch, do you prefer pizza, pan-fried crab cakes, a big salad of organic greens topped with a pancetta-wrapped roasted salmon filet, or a vegetarian pasta with a roasted chili sauce? Chef Mark Stark, a graduate of the Culinary Institute of America and veteran of numerous Washington, D.C., restaurants, brings a sophisticated cross-cultural punch to a large menu that changes more frequently than the seasons. ♦ Likewise, the choice of seating is bound to please. You can sit in the main "barn" with its high white rafters and view of the busy open kitchen, two smaller rooms filled with paintings, or an outdoor patio sheltered by canvas umbrellas and surrounded by flowers. Service is speedy and polite throughout, and an all-California wine list has plenty to offer by the glass as well as the bottle.

AVERAGE DINNER FOR TWO: $50
DOES NOT INCLUDE WINE, TAX AND GRATUITY

CHEF CHU'S

1067 NORTH SAN ANTONIO ROAD
AT EL CAMINO REAL
LOS ALTOS, CA 94022
(415) 948-2696

Visa & Major Credit Cards
Open Daily • Lunch & Dinner

Manager
CHARLIE ONG

Chef/Proprietor
LAWRENCE CHU

Recommended Items

Appetizers
CATFISH ROLL
• CRISPY-FRIED SHRIMP
BALLS • MINCED CHICKEN
• POTSTICKERS • SMOKED FISH
SHANGHAI-STYLE

Entrées
PEKING DUCK
• SZECHUAN-STYLE DRY
BRAISED PRAWNS • MU
SHU PORK • PRAWNS WITH
CANDIED PECANS IN LIGHT
MUSTARD SAUCE • BRAISED
WHOLE FRESH FISH

CHEF CHU'S, LOCATED IN THE HEART OF THE PENINSULA'S EL Camino Real nightlife, is celebrating its twenty-fifth anniversary and has kept current with Chinese cuisine that reflects a new era of fresh, nutritious and unpretentious food. In the downstairs bar and dining room, the mood is bustling, upbeat and fun. The upstairs dining room is more formal, with a magnificent wood carving of The Nine Dragons covering an entire wall. ♦ Author of the bestselling *Chef Chu's Distinctive Cuisine of China*, Chef Lawrence Chu is the guiding force behind this restaurant. "To enjoy food," says Chu, "you must be relaxed, in a good mood and in the proper atmosphere." ♦ Chu's spirit is everywhere; he can be seen in the spotless kitchen preparing "Lover's Prawns" for newlyweds or in the lobby, scrawling a Chinese birthday greeting on the signboard for an 86-year-old guest. Chef Chu is frequently seen on television sharing his wok cooking skills, and is more than happy to advise his patrons in menu planning.

AVERAGE DINNER FOR TWO: $30
DOES NOT INCLUDE WINE, TAX AND GRATUITY

EMILE'S

545 SOUTH SECOND STREET
SAN JOSE, CA 95112
(408) 289-1960

Visa & Major Credit Cards
Dinner Tues-Sat • Lunch Fri Only

Manager
CHERYL MARTINEZ

Chef/Proprietor
EMILE MOOSER
Chef de Cuisine
JAMES CONNOLLY

Recommended Items

♦♦

Appetizers

PEPPERED & CHARRED AHI
WITH RADISH SPROUTS
• HOUSE-CURED GRAVLAX
SERVED WITH YOGURT DILL
SAUCE & ONION COMPOTE

Entrées

ROASTED WILD BOAR
"SOUS VIDE" WITH FRESH
FRUIT COMPOTE • FRESH
STURGEON, DRY-BAKED IN A
LEMON VERBENA HERB CRUST
WITH FLAGEOLET BEANS,
TOMATOES & CAPERS

CELEBRATING HIS TWENTY-SECOND YEAR IN DOWNTOWN San Jose, Chef Emile Mooser says, "My formal training in the wine country above Lake Geneva taught me the intricacies of the classic marriage of food and wine." Reflecting today's lifestyle, he now emphasizes "Cuisine Minceur," a light, healthy approach to cooking that doesn't sacrifice taste. His managerial skills ensure meticulous service. ♦ Chef de Cuisine James Connolly has worked closely for twelve years to articulate Chef Emile Mooser's culinary philosophy and commitment to quality. Recently the restaurant was remodeled and generously expanded, enabling it to provide even more of the intimate, elegant setting that so perfectly highlights the cuisine and extensive wine collection.

AVERAGE DINNER FOR TWO: $60
DOES NOT INCLUDE WINE, TAX AND GRATUITY

VIP

ITALIAN/SEAFOOD

FISHERMAN BAR & GRILL

1492 OLD BAYSHORE HIGHWAY
OFF HIGHWAY 101
BURLINGAME, CA 94010
(415) 548-1490

Visa & Major Credit Cards
Open Daily for Dinner • Lunch Mon-Sat

Proprietors
RICHARD PATANE

Chef
JOHN ALEXANDER
CLARK

Recommended Items

Appetizers

•WOOD-OVEN-BAKED OYSTERS
STUFFED WITH SPINACH, SHAL-
LOTS, OLIVE OIL &
FRESH BREADCRUMBS,
FRESH HORSERADISH SAUCE

• HOUSE-CURED SALMON
GRAVLAX WITH DILL & MUS-
TARD SAUCE

Entrées

• SAUTÉED CALAMARI WITH
GARLIC, PARSLEY, WHITE WINE
& ROASTED POLENTA

• FISHERMAN CRAB CIOPPINO

• FRESH FETTUCINE WITH
SCALLOPS & LEMON SAUCE

LOCATED JUST SOUTH OF THE AIRPORT, FISHERMAN BAR & GRILL rewards every diner with a panoramic view of San Francisco Bay. At low tide, sandpipers and rare water birds forage for food. In the evening, lights in the distant East Bay hills sparkle. Day and night, planes take off and land in a mesmerizing flow, their sound completely muffled by a thick glass wall that runs the length of the restaurant. ♦ The Fisherman's multi-leveled interior echoes its idyllic waterfront setting. Canvas softens the overhead lighting, frescoes of sea life enliven the warm cream walls, and copper and mahogany finishes add an elegant nautical touch, of warmth throughout. ♦ Chef John Alexander Clark makes full use of the large exhibition kitchen and its wood-fired oven and grill. He favors Italian-style grilling for fish and vegetables and is a master of Neopolitan-style pizza and fresh pasta. John's fragrant shellfish risotto, with mussels, shrimp, squid and clams, is a must-try. ♦ With jazz piano in the lounge and two large private rooms, Fisherman Bar & Grill is as suitable for a romantic Saturday night as it is for a corporate party.

AVERAGE DINNER FOR TWO: $52
DOES NOT INCLUDE WINE, TAX AND GRATUITY

Add some sparkle to your meals.

S.PELLEGRINO

Sparkling Natural Mineral Water
Bottled at the Source, San Pellegrino, Italy.
Since 1899.

You absolutely deserve to eat in one of these great restaurants. That is, of course, if you can make up your mind as to which one before they all close for the night.

AMSTEL *light*

Flower Lounge

51 Millbrae Avenue
AT EL CAMINO REAL
Millbrae, CA 94030
(415) 692-6666

Visa & Major Credit Cards
Open Daily • Lunch & Dinner

Proprietor
Alice Wong

Chef
Chan Tit Wan

Recommended Items

Appetizers
Shredded duck with
fresh fruits • Chicken
salad rainbow • Fried
seafood with crispy nest
• Squab braised in beer

Entrées
Fried prawns with glazed
walnuts in special sauce
• Baked crab Hunan-style
• Braised tofu with minced
shrimp • Shredded beef
in black pepper sauce
with green onions
• Squab with mango

WHEN ALICE WONG FIRST CAME TO THE BAY AREA TO STUDY economics at Mills College, she expected to join her family's garment business after graduation. Upon her return to Hong Kong, however, she found her family had started a successful chain of celebrated restaurants called Flower Lounge. That was all it took to change her plans. ♦ An ambitious woman, Wong set out to change the American conception of Cantonese food as bland, with little to offer besides unexciting egg rolls and chop suey. She returned to the Bay Area to open the first Flower Lounge outside Hong Kong. ♦ Chef Chan Tit Wan creates the subtly spiced, seafood-dominant dishes that are the trademarks of authentic Cantonese haute cuisine. "We spend more time on preparation and less on actual cooking, so that the natural flavors of the ingredients are retained, not masked," says Wong.

AVERAGE DINNER FOR TWO: $30
DOES NOT INCLUDE WINE, TAX AND GRATUITY

LE MOUTON NOIR

14560 BIG BASIN WAY
NEAR HIGHWAY NINE
SARATOGA, CA 95070
(408) 867-7017
Visa & Major Credit Cards
Dinner Daily • Lunch Saturday

Proprietor
DON DURANTE

Chef
DEB CONWAY

Recommended Items

Appetizers
WILD MUSHROOM SALAD
WITH GOAT CHEESE
• CARPACCIO OF CURED AHI
TUNA WITH GIN & TOASTED
ANISE SEEDS • BRAISED
RABBIT & BRIE CHEESE
CANNELONI WITH CAYENNE
PEPPER SABAYON
Entrées
DUCK A LA MOUTON
NOIR • ROASTED RACK OF
LAMB WITH CELERY ROOT
TATIN • NIGHTLY FRESH
FISH SPECIALS

CONTRARY TO WHAT ITS NAME IMPLIES, LE MOUTON NOIR IS certainly not "the black sheep" of Saratoga's famous restaurant row. Located in an historic 140-year-old Victorian decorated with Laura Ashley prints, colorful sprays of flowers and tones of pink and dusty rose, this dining establishment has the cheerfulness of a country home. The place is a favorite with local restaurant connoisseurs. ♦ Proprietor Don Durante and Chef Deb Conway plan the seasonal menus together and rely on local producers for most of their fish, vegetables and herbs. ♦ "It's contemporary French-inspired California cuisine," says Durante. "We try to be very progressive, very innovative." The kitchen's *à la minute* preparation technique captures the full flavor of the fresh seafood, vegetables, beef and prime lamb.

AVERAGE DINNER FOR TWO: $65
DOES NOT INCLUDE WINE, TAX AND GRATUITY

VIP

LE PAPILLON

410 SARATOGA AVENUE
AT KIELY & OFF HWY 280
SAN JOSE, CA 95129
(408) 296-3730

Visa & Major Credit Cards
Open Daily for Dinner • Lunch Mon–Fri

Proprietor
MIKE MASHAYEKH

Chef
SCOTT COOPER

Recommended Items

Appetizers
BROILED SCALLOPS
IN CAJUN SPICE & CREAM
• GRILLED LOBSTER
WITH LIME BUTTER SAUCE
• FETTUCCINE WITH WILD
MUSHROOMS & TOASTED
PECANS

Entrées
MEDALLIONS OF RED DEER
IN CABERNET TRUFFLE SAUCE
• AHI TUNA WITH COCONUT
MILK, LEMON GRASS & CURRY
• GRILLED SWORDFISH WITH
JALAPEÑOS, LIME & CREAM

WHEN MIKE MASHAYEKH OPENED LE PAPILLON RESTAURANT IN 1977, over eighteen years ago, he would not have imagined that some day his step son, Scott Cooper, would take over the kitchen of his well established restaurant. It's been more than 5 years now since Chef Scott did take over and led this traditional French restaurant to new and different directions. ♦ Scott's knowledge and creativity has gradually propelled this restaurant to another level that has brought much recognition to Le Papillon. One of the chef's main talents lies in his ability to take fine and unique ingredients and prepare them in his own special and innovative style. In addition Scott's remarkable attitude and thirst for perfection drives him to pay special attention to every aspect of food preparation. It is no surprise then when dining at Le Papillon for lunch or dinner, you'll find yourself enriched and enraptured by the experience.

AVERAGE DINNER FOR TWO: $60
DOES NOT INCLUDE WINE, TAX AND GRATUITY

PAOLO'S RESTAURANT

333 WEST SAN CARLOS STREET
SAN JOSE, CA 95110
(408) 294-2558

Visa & Major Credit Cards
Lunch Mon-Fri • Dinner Mon-Sat

Proprietor
CAROLYN ALLEN
Maitre d'/General Manager
JALIL SAMAVARCHIAN

Proprietor
JENNY ALLEN-
GRIESBACH

Recommended Items

Appetizers

GUINEA FOWL PATÉ WITH
MARINATED MUSHROOMS &
ASPARAGUS TIPS • SMOKED
STURGEON WITH HORSERADISH
CREAM, RED ONION & CRACKED
BELL PEPPER

Entrées

GRILLED VEAL CHOP WITH
WHITEBEAN & SAGE PURÉE
• POACHED STRIPED BASS IN
BROTH WITH CLAMS,
TOMATOES, PRUNES & PINE
NUTS • ROASTED RABBIT
WITH WHITE WINE, MORELS,
BEETS & SAUTÉED GREENS

FOUNDER JACK ALLEN'S DAUGHTERS, CAROLYN ALLEN-Samavarchian and Jenny Allen-Griesbach, are guiding Paolo's into a new era. In its new location at RiverPark, Paolo's boasts a relaxed atmosphere in a park-like setting. Maitre d' Jalil Samavarchian oversees a beautifully appointed dining room that incorporates warm, rich tones, dramatic touches and European style. ♦ The diverse wine list includes more than 450 California, Italian and French selections as well as an extensive vintage Port collection. The kitchen insists on authenticity in ingredients and flavor in Paolo's contemporary adaption of classic regional Italian cuisine. The family travels frequently to the Italian provinces for in-depth research into regional foods and wines. ♦ The unique and varied bar menu makes a quick breakfast or lunch, and early or late night snack. It is deliciously affordable and especially convenient for dining before or after the theatre. To create a memorable event private dining is available for groups of 10 to 125.

AVERAGE DINNER FOR TWO: $50
DOES NOT INCLUDE WINE, TAX AND GRATUITY

231 ELLSWORTH

231 SOUTH ELLSWORTH STREET
AT THIRD AVENUE
SAN MATEO, CA 94401
(415) 347-7231
Visa & Major Credit Cards
Dinner Mon-Sat • Lunch Mon-Fri

Proprietors
KEN OTTOBONI

Chef
DEREK BURNS
ANDREW MANN
PHIL OGIELA

Recommended Items

Appetizers
HOUSE-SMOKED RABBIT
WITH PEAR BRÛLÉE
• OYSTERS ON THE HALFSHELL
WITH LEMON SORBET VODKA
• WARM GOAT CHEESE
CROTTIN WITH BLACK PEPPER
PUFF PASTRY

Entrées
FILET OF BEEF WITH WILD
MUSHROOM TART, MADEIRA &
TRUFFLES • ROASTED SALMON
WITH TAPENADE & GREEN
SAUCE • ROASTED SQUAB OVER
LENTILS, BRAISED CABBAGE &
CHANTERELLES

FOR EIGHT STRAIGHT YEARS, 231 ELLSWORTH HAS WON THE *San Francisco Focus* People's Choice Award for finest restaurant on the Peninsula in any category. ♦ The restaurant's well-deserved place in the spotlight reflects customer appreciation for its modern versions of French cuisine and well-chosen collection of 600 French and California wines. This, along with proprietor Ken Ottoboni's gracious dining room supervision, create a complete fine dining experience. ♦ Under the watchful eye of Derek Burns, Andrew Mann uses only the freshest and finest ingredients to orchestrate seasonal à la carte and prix-fixe lunch and dinner menus. Besides the widely acclaimed desserts of Phil Ogiela, mushrooms have become another trademark at 231. No wonder – Ken Ottoboni owns a wild mushroom company that delivers fresh porcini, chanterelles, morels and other edibles weekly, enabling the restaurant to serve more varieties than perhaps any other in the country!

AVERAGE DINNER FOR TWO: $60
DOES NOT INCLUDE WINE, TAX AND GRATUITY

Meadowood
Napa Valley

A World Apart in the Napa Valley

Fireplace Suites, The Grill,
The Restaurant, Tennis,
Golf, Croquet, Pools,
Hiking Trails, Wine School,
The Health Spa

Meadowood Resort • 900 Meadowood Lane • St. Helena, CA 94574
TEL (707) 963-3646 FAX (707) 963-3532

PREFERRED HOTELS

RELAIS &
CHATEAUX

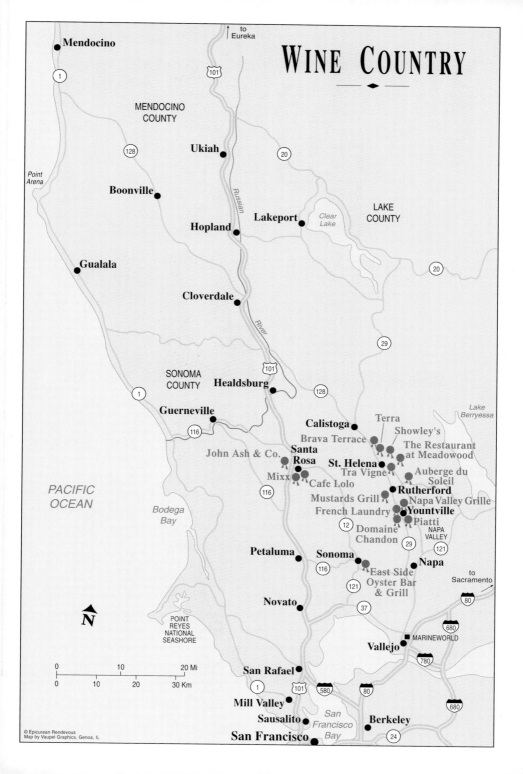

WINE COUNTRY

to
Eureka

Mendocino

1

MENDOCINO
COUNTY

101

Ukiah

20

Point
Arena

128

Boonville

Russian

Hopland

Lakeport

Clear
Lake

LAKE
COUNTY

Gualala

20

Cloverdale

River

29

SONOMA
COUNTY

101

Healdsburg

128

1

Guerneville

116

Lake
Berryessa

Calistoga

Terra

Showley's

Brava Terrace

The Restaurant
at Meadowood

PACIFIC
OCEAN

John Ash & Co.

Santa
Rosa

St. Helena

Tra Vigne

Auberge du
Soleil

Mixx

Cafe Lolo

Rutherford

Bodega
Bay

116

Mustards Grill

Napa Valley Grille

French Laundry

Yountville

Piatti

12

Domaine
Chandon

29

NAPA
VALLEY

121

Petaluma

Sonoma

Napa

116

East Side
Oyster Bar
& Grill

to
Sacramento

121

Novato

37

80

N

POINT
REYES
NATIONAL
SEASHORE

Vallejo

MARINEWORLD

680

780

| 0 | 10 | 20 Mi |
| 0 | 10 | 20 | 30 Km |

San Rafael

1

Mill Valley

101

580

80

680

Sausalito

San
Francisco
Bay

Berkeley

San Francisco

24

© Epicurean Rendevous
Map by Vaupel Graphics, Genoa, IL

AUBERGE DU SOLEIL

180 RUTHERFORD HILL ROAD
RUTHERFORD, CA 94573
(707) 963-1211

Visa & Major Credit Cards
Open Daily • Breakfast, Lunch & Dinner

General Manager
GEORGE A. GOEGGEL

Chef
ANDREW SUTTON

Recommended Items

Appetizers
THYME ROASTED PHEASANT
RAVIOLI, WOODLAND MUSH-
ROOMS, LEMON-MAPLE
GLAZE • HICKORY SMOKED
SHRIMP, BLACK BEAN RELISH,
LIME-CHIPOTLE SAUCE

Entrées
GRILLED PACIFIC SALMON,
CARAMELIZED PEARL ONIONS,
LOBSTER BORDELAISE
• BACON ROASTED VENISON
LOIN, ROSEMARY BARLEY,
RED PEPPER SAUCE

AUBERGE DU SOLEIL —"THE INN OF THE SUN"— IS A WONDERFULLY
romantic country inn set among the hills of Napa Valley. The restaurant's cedar columns and rough-timbered ceilings contrast sharply
with the French doors, pink tablecloths and bouquets of wildflowers
that are thoroughly Provençal in style. Then there's the deck. Fifteen
tables overlook the glorious Napa Valley, a 160-degree panorama of
olive groves, terraced vineyards and rolling foothills, which, when late
afternoon turns amber, could easily be the golden hills of Tuscany. It's
easy to see why the deck is the preferred spot to dine, or to just sip a
glass of wine. ♦ Executive Chef Andrew Sutton's Texas roots and
California culinary experience inspire an enchanting mix of contrasts,
blended to embrace Napa Valley's diversity. A proponent of using only
the freshest local ingredients, Sutton creates wine country cuisine that
highlights Napa's bountiful produce and the valley's adaptations of
culinary influences from all over the world.

AVERAGE DINNER FOR TWO: $85
DOES NOT INCLUDE WINE, TAX AND GRATUITY

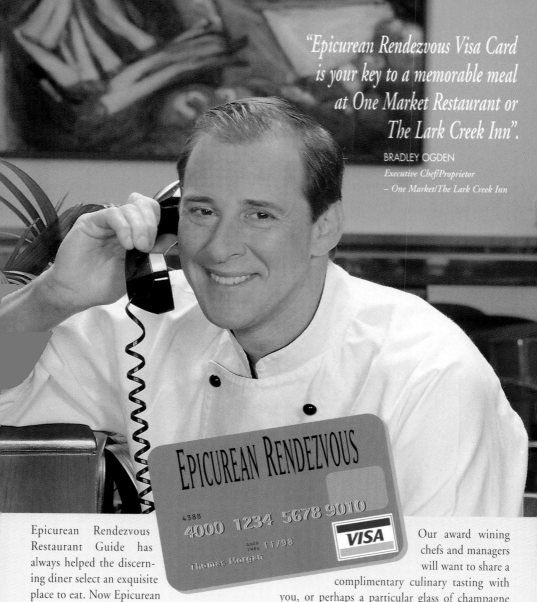

"Epicurean Rendezvous Visa Card
is your key to a memorable meal
at One Market Restaurant or
The Lark Creek Inn".

BRADLEY OGDEN
*Executive Chef/Proprietor
– One Market/The Lark Creek Inn*

EPICUREAN RENDEZVOUS

4388
4000 1234 5678 9010

GOOD
THRU 11/98

Thomas Morgan

VISA

Epicurean Rendezvous Restaurant Guide has always helped the discerning diner select an exquisite place to eat. Now Epicurean Rendezvous and Visa have introduced the perfect accompaniment to any dining experience – The Epicurean Rendezvous Visa Gold Card. As an Epicurean Rendezvous Visa card holder, you can expect various kinds of special and individual treatment, from the time you first identify yourself on the telephone to the last personal good-bye you receive at the door.

Our award wining chefs and managers will want to share a complimentary culinary tasting with you, or perhaps a particular glass of champagne or wine that best enhances your meal. You will receive recognition and personal attention throughout the meal. And, at many of our restaurants you will be given preferred seating and guaranteed on-time reservations. Order your Epicurean Rendezvous Visa Gold Card today, and get paid the perfect compliment.

THE CARD THAT COMPLEMENTS EVERY MEAL.

BRAVA TERRACE

3010 St. Helena Highway North
St. Helena, CA 94574
(707) 963-9300

Visa & Major Credit Cards
Open Daily • Lunch & Dinner
(Served continuously throughout the day)

Proprietor
DEBBIE HALPERT

Chef/Proprietor
FRED HALPERT

Recommended Items

Appetizers
PROVENÇAL SALAD OF WILD
GREENS & HERBS WITH WARM
SONOMA GOAT CHEESE ON A
CROUTON • GRILLED
PORTOBELLO MUSHROOMS,
SPINACH & GARLIC WALNUT
VINAIGRETTE
• SPICY PEPPERED &
FRIED OYSTERS

Entrées
GRILLED FRESH FISH SPECIALLY
PREPARED DAILY • COQ-AU-VIN
• GRILLED VEAL CHOP, RAGOUT
OF LOCAL MUSHROOMS &
TARRAGON AU JUS

A TREMENDOUS HIT SINCE IT FIRST OPENED, BRAVA TERRACE HAS perfected its evocation of Southern France's sunny insouciance. The airy dining room is immediately engaging, and so is the namesake terrace overlooking Napa Valley's vineyards. But it's the kitchen that best hails the luminous spirit of Provence. ♦ Chef/Owner Fred Halpert creates romantic specialities influenced by that special region of France known for light natural ingredients, but enhanced with robust flavor and seasonings. One of the more classic French dishes is Fred's signature cassolet – a generous stew of French lentils, pork tenderloin, chicken and local turkey sausage simmer for hours in homemade veal stock. ♦ Although Fred was taught by such masters as Alain Chapel, Roger Vergé, Jacques Maximin and Alain Senderens, Brava Terrace is fun and unpretentious. Prices are reasonable and Fred's cooking style (which diners can observe as he works in the open kitchen) is relaxed. He calls his menu of California and French cooking "cuisines of the sun," using produce plucked fresh from the restaurant's own garden.

AVERAGE DINNER FOR TWO: $40
DOES NOT INCLUDE WINE, TAX AND GRATUITY

CAFE LOLO

620 FIFTH STREET
AT MENDOCINO
SANTA ROSA, CA 95494
(707) 576-7822
Visa & Major Credit Cards
Dinner Mon-Sat • Lunch Mon-Fri

Proprietor/Chef
MICHAEL QUIGLEY

Proprietor/Manager
LORI DARLING

Recommended Items

Appetizers

AHI CARPACCIO W/SOY-WHITE
TRUFFLE OIL VINAIGRETTE

• WARM FLAN OF LAURA CHENEL
GOAT CHEESE W/SWEET & SOUR
ONION RELISH & GRILLED BREAD

Entrées

PAN-SEARED SCALLOPS
W/ROASTED BEETS, WILD MUSH-
ROOMS & ARTICHOKE PANCAKES

• PAN-ROASTED LIBERTY DUCK
BREAST W/CABBAGE, APPLES,
PANCETTA, POTATO GALETTE &
HONEY-THYME ESSENCE

THERE IS A HAPPY FEELING AT CAFE LOLO, A SENSE OF HARMONY and well-being. It begins with the owners, Michael Quigley and Lori Darling ("Lolo"), who exude the *joie de vivre* of a young couple doing what they love. It extends to the staff, who smile and greet customers by name. And it culminates in the laughter and high spirits that fill this airy California-style bistro. ♦ Since it opened in August of 1993, Cafe Lolo has earned critical praise and a loyal clientele. After stints at the Sheraton Palace in San Francisco and the Meadowood Resort in the Napa Valley, Chef Quigley fell under the spell of his wife's native Sonoma County. Here, he transforms the area's rich seasonal bounty into sophisticated dishes with California spirit and French backbone. Flavors mesh with seamless assertion, plates are attractive yet unfussy, and portions are generous. His osso bucco, for example, is a tender veal shank atop a pungent mixture of white beans and black and green olives in an earthy, addictive sauce. ♦ True to Cafe Lolo's local roots, the award-winning wine list is 95% Sonoma County wines, all superbly priced.

AVERAGE DINNER FOR TWO: $45
DOES NOT INCLUDE WINE, TAX AND GRATUITY

VIP

DOMAINE CHANDON

CALIFORNIA DRIVE
AT HIGHWAY 29
YOUNTVILLE, CA 94599
(707) 944-2892 • (800) 736-2892

Visa & Major Credit Cards
Closed Monday & Tuesday • Lunch & Dinner

Manager
MARIO DANIELE

Chef
PHILIPPE JEANTY

Recommended Items

Appetizers
HOUSE-SMOKED RED
TROUT FILET MARINATED
IN OLIVE OIL & ONIONS
• MANILA CLAMS STEAMED
IN SPARKLING WINE

Entrées
GRILLED SALMON
WRAPPED IN PANCETTA
• VENISON TOURNEDOES WITH
SWEET POTATO NAPOLEON
• ROASTED PAINE FARM
SQUAB WITH WHITE CORN &
BACON POTATOES

WHEN THE GREAT HOUSE OF CHAMPAGNE, MOET ET CHANDON, came to the United States and established Domaine Chandon in the high-profile Napa Valley, oenophiles expected a great American sparkling wine, and they have not been disappointed. They got even more than they bargained for: a fine French restaurant. ♦ Chef Philippe Jeanty of Epernay, France, trained in the heart of Champagne, was appointed Chef de Cuisine at Domaine Chandon in 1978. "I style my cuisine to reflect California's openness to innovation, the readily available fresh products and the great traditions of French cooking," he says. "And," he adds with a sparkle in his eyes, "I emphasize foods compatible with Champagne." For dessert, the banana split with almond croquant ice cream or polenta pudding soaked in blueberries are unique theme variations. ♦ Manager and Maître d' Mario Daniele maintains Moët et Chandon's 250-year tradition of hospitality, presenting the cuisine with professional flair but without unnecessary flourish.

AVERAGE DINNER FOR TWO: $90
DOES NOT INCLUDE WINE, TAX AND GRATUITY

EastSide Oyster Bar & Grill

133 EAST NAPA STREET
SONOMA, CA 95476
(707) 939-1266

Visa & Major Credit Cards
Open Daily • Lunch & Dinner • Sunday Brunch

Manager
KATY HANRATTY

Chef/Proprietor
CHARLES SAUNDERS

Recommended Items

Appetizers
PETALUMA DUCK
TASTING PLATE
• FRIED OYSTERS WITH
MOROCCAN BARBECUE SAUCE
• SAFFRON PASTA, JUMBO
ROCK SHRIMP, ASPARAGUS
TIPS & PINE NUTS
Entrées
GIANT CALIFORNIA
SALMON & CRAB SUSHI ROLL
WITH TEMPURA VEGETABLES
• CK RANCH LAMB PARFAIT
ON CHICK PEA MASH,
ONION CONFIT & ROASTED
PLUM TOMATOES
• VEGETARIAN MAIN PLATE

IN SUMMER, THE BEST SPOT TO DINE AT EASTSIDE OYSTER BAR &
Grill is out back on the patio. A kumquat and walnut tree provide shade at
lunch and after dusk, tiny golden lights enhance the grape arbor under
which you can experience some of the most inspired cooking in a region
dedicated to food and wine. Guests can enjoy the intimate indoor dining
room with fireplace year round. ♦ Proud owner and kitchen muse Charles
Saunders maintains a holistic approach to creating his meals. The Culinary
Institute of America and Sonoma Mission Inn veteran believes in the "rip-
ple effect," and likens EastSide to "a small stone tossed into a still pond."
In other words, he wants to make a difference, to create a landmark that
guests will return to again and again. Pride in local artisans, produce, wines
and true culinary integrity are the key ingredients here. "We select what's
fresh from the vine, the farm and the sea." ♦ Although the California menu
leans toward seafood, the large selection of other products at Saunders's
fingertips invites experimentation. Notable locals have already made this a
regular stop, raving about the restaurant's innovative presentation and
light, multicultural specialties.

AVERAGE DINNER FOR TWO: $50
DOES NOT INCLUDE WINE, TAX AND GRATUITY

VIP

THE FRENCH LAUNDRY

6640 WASHINGTON STREET
AT CREEK
YOUNTVILLE, CA 94599
(707) 944-2380
Visa & Major Credit Cards
Closed Monday • Dinner Only

Proprietor/Chef
THOMAS KELLER

General Manager
LAURA G.
CUNNINGHAM

Recommended Items

Appetizers

WARM FRICASSEE OF ARTI-
CHOKES & VEGETABLES W/ROSE-
MARY-INFUSED EXTRA VIRGIN OIL
• "TONGUE-IN-CHEEK" SALAD
W/BABY LEEKS, CONFIT OF
TOMATOES & GARDEN GREENS,
HORSERADISH CREAM

Entrées

RICE-PAPER-WRAPPED ATLANTIC
SALMON W/SEVRUGA CAVIAR &
LEMON BEURRE BLANC • PAN-
SEARED DUCK BREAST W/MOREL
MUSHROOMS & CREAMED YEL-
LOW CORN & SLOW COOKED
VEAL BREAST W/ROASTED ROOT
VEGETABLES & GLAZED GARLIC

SINCE 1994, WHEN THOMAS KELLER TOOK OVER AS CHEF/OWNER of The French Laundry, food lovers have converged on the small stone landmark built in the 1900s as a laundry. Attended by a young, highly polished staff, diners savor a succession of five small courses chosen from a changing menu. Each dish glorifies the essence of its ingredients in artful yet simple arrangements. Before dinner has even begun, an eggshell filled with an ambrosia of white truffle custard and black truffle ragout arrives with a potato "chip." Everything that follows is just as sophisticated, pure and intense. ♦ Although the focus is on the food, the atmosphere is friendly rather than formal. Light taupe walls and large floral arrangements create a soothing background for leisurely dining, and a manicured garden accommodates a few tables on warm nights. ♦ Lauded for his cooking at Checkers in Los Angeles and Rakel in New York City, Thomas learned his precise style in the top kitchens of France. For dessert, his cappucino semifreddo with a mini-doughnut is outstanding, as is the warm chocolate truffle cake. The wine list, including outstanding reserve and limited-production selections, is an oenophile's dream.

AVERAGE DINNER FOR TWO: $114
DOES NOT INCLUDE WINE, TAX AND GRATUITY

JOHN ASH & CO.

4330 BARNES ROAD
HIGHWAY 101 AT RIVER ROAD
SANTA ROSA, CA 95403
(707) 527-7687

Visa • MasterCard • American Express Only
Dinner Daily • Lunch Tues-Sun

General Manager
STEPHEN THRUSH
Managing Partner
JOHN P. DUFFY

Chef
JEFFREY MADURA
Consulting Chef
JOHN ASH

Recommended Items

Appetizers
SONOMA ONION SOUP
• CHORIZO SAUSAGE CALZONE
• DEEP FRIED CALAMARI
• CAESAR SALAD

Entrées
PENNE PASTA WITH PORTABELLO
MUSHROOMS • DUNGENESS
CRAB CAKES • FILET OF BEEF
WITH ROASTED GARLIC
MASHED POTATOES

"WINE COUNTRY CUISINE", COINED BY JOHN ASH WHEN HE opened 15 years ago, still explains the style of food presented at this beautiful, nationally acclaimed restaurant located amidst a 45-acre vineyard. Chef Jeffrey Madura has blended Ash's creative use of Sonoma County's incredible bounty and his own home-style sensitivity to produce an ever-changing menu that provides warm and delicious dining options for both the eyes and the taste buds. ♦ In the winter, the dining room is warm and inviting with cozy fireplaces, sweeping views of the vineyards and colorful art, while warmer weather provides the opportunity for delightful heated outdoor terrace dining. John Ash & Co. shares this beautiful setting with Vintners Inn, a charming 44-room, European-style hotel. ♦ The restaurant features an award-winning wine list, a full bar and cafe dinner every afternoon. Monday dining begins at 5:30 pm and Sunday brunch is served at 10:30am.

AVERAGE DINNER FOR TWO: $50
DOES NOT INCLUDE WINE, TAX AND GRATUITY

MIXX

135 FOURTH STREET
SANTA ROSA, CA 95401
(707) 573-1344

Visa & Major Credit Cards
Dinner Daily • Lunch Mon-Fri

Proprietor/Pastry Chef
KATHLEEN BERMAN

Chef/Proprietor
DAN BERMAN

Recommended Items

Appetizers
GRILLED FRESH OYSTERS W/
ROASTED TOMATO SALSA &
VELLA DRY AGED JACK CHEESE
• GRILLED NEW MEXICO
CHILIES STUFFED W/
BELLWETHER FARMS PECORINO
& RICOTTA CHEESE

Entrées
SONOMA LIBERTY DUCK BREAST
W/A HONEY, CHILE-PASTE &
TAMARIND GLAZE, SERVED W/A
WARM SOBA NOODLE SALAD,
PICKLED CABBAGE & GINGER
POACHED ASIAN PEAR • FILET
OF SALMON OVEN ROASTED ON
CEDAR PLANK & SERVED W/RED
& GREEN TOMATO RELISH

"SONOMA FRESH" DESCRIBES THE CUISINE OF MIXX. SONOMA was county the perfect place to develop the innovative and ever-changing fare of MIXX restaurant, with its excellent produce, local meat, fish and award-winning wine list. ♦ When Dan and Kathleen Berman, classmates and graduates of the California Culinary Academy, realized their ambition of opening an upscale but unpretentious bistro, they put their love and attention into every detail. The result is an Art Nouveau atmosphere, with a 19th century hand-carved mahogany bar and the brightness of a modern establishment. ♦ With much of their produce brought to the back door by local farmers, the menu always has seasonal surprises. Yet, locals like to make their favorite dishes known and, consequently, can usually find them at MIXX. As co-owners and operators, Dan does further duty as Executive Chef and Kathleen as Pastry Chef. MIXX was the spot chosen for lunch during Julia Child's recent visit to Sonoma County.

AVERAGE DINNER FOR TWO: $45
DOES NOT INCLUDE WINE, TAX AND GRATUITY

VIP

FREEDOM

OF VODKA

STOLICHNAYA

Stolichnaya
Ohranj

1 LITER
35% ALC. VOL.
(70 PROOF)

ORANGE FLAVORED
RUSSIAN VODKA

MUSTARDS GRILL

7399 St. Helena Highway 29
Yountville, Ca 94558
(707) 944-2424

Visa & Major Credit Cards
Open Daily • Lunch & Dinner

Managing Partner
MICHAEL OUELLETE

Executive Chef
GREG GEVURTZ

Recommended Items

Appetizers

"BUCKEYE" SMOKED SALMON
POSILLA, CORN CAKES & CREME
FRAICHE, CRISPY CALAMARI &
CURY SLAW • SEARED RARE AHI
TUNA WITH WASABI CREAM ON
SESAME CRACKERS

Entrées

GRILLED RABBIT CACCIATORE
• LAMB SHANK BRAISED WITH
BLOCKHEADIA RINGNOSII
ZINFADEL • GRILLED AHI
TUNA SANDWICH WITH BASIL
MAYONNAISE & GINGER

REAL RESTAURANTS PARTNERS BILL HIGGINS, BILL UPSON AND Cindy Pawlcyn, realizing the restaurant kitchen is the new theatre in American life, placed an open cooking area with an oak and almond-burning grill and oven in the middle of their lively Napa Valley restaurant. ◆ Continuing the spirit and tradition established by founding Chef Cindy Pawlcyn, Chef Greg Gevurtz enjoys the freedom he has at the restaurant to be highly creative. He likes food that apperas simple, but often requires more complex preparation; such as the many smoked and marinated items on the menu. Chef Greg's dishes are stylish and light, characterized by unusual herbs, grilled fish, smoked meats and the North Coast's abundant boutique vegetables. ◆ The ambiance at Mustards is lively and youthful. A new outdoor "Cigar and Wildlife Preserve" is an intriguing addition to the fun, and Managing Partner Michael Ouellete's intelligent wine list draws local winemakers. You'll often find them at the bar sipping one of the many Napa Valley varietals available by the glass.

AVERAGE DINNER FOR TWO: $40
DOES NOT INCLUDE WINE, TAX AND GRATUITY

NAPA VALLEY GRILLE

6795 WASHINGTON STREET
HIGHWAY 29 AT MADISON
YOUNTVILLE, CA 94599
(707) 944-8686

Visa & Major Credit Cards
Open Daily • Lunch & Dinner • Sunday Brunch

General Manager
MICHAEL STEINHART

Chef
ROBERT THOMAS
HURLEY

Recommended Items

Appetizers
CRISPY MIX OF CALAMARI, ROCK SHRIMP & ARTICHOKES, SPICY REMOULADE • SPICY LINGUINE W/JUMBO PRAWNS, PANCETTA, FRESH PLUM TOMATOES, CARAMELIZED ONIONS, PARMESAN

Entrées
GRILLED ATLANTIC SALMON W/ARTICHOKES, BLACK OLIVES, ROASTED GARLIC, SUNDRIED TOMATOES & FINGERLING POTATOES • PEPPER-CRUSTED RACK OF PORK W/POTATO, LEEK & GOAT CHEESE GRATIN & APRICOT, PINENUT & PEARL ONION COMPOTE

WHEN YOU CRAVE BRIGHT SUNSHINE, TRANQUIL VINEYARDS and a profusion of flowers, head for the Napa Valley Grille. Set in Yountville's delightful Washington Square, its stone facade epitomizes the rustic beauty of the Napa Valley. Yet like the Valley itself, this inviting restaurant combines country charm with city know-how, most notably in a menu and wine list that glorify the best the region has to offer. ♦ And that's a lot! Winner of the Wine Spectator Award of Excellence, the wine list is a who's who of the top vintners in the area and beyond. To showcase the wine selection, Chef Bob Hurley, a veteran of Auberge du Soleil and Domaine Chandon, boldly combines the finest local products in a Mediterranean-inspired style. Often grilled, his main ingredients share center stage with such imaginative enhancements as pineapple-jalapeño salsa, fire-roasted onions and sundried cranberry chutney. ♦ With its exhibition kitchen and wine displays, the Napa Valley Grille's plush dining room is always welcoming. But on a warm day, the patio is the perfect place to savor both the fine food and unique beauty of the Napa Valley.

AVERAGE DINNER FOR TWO: $55
DOES NOT INCLUDE WINE, TAX AND GRATUITY

PIATTI

6480 WASHINGTON STREET
YOUNTVILLE, CA 94599
(707) 944-2070
Visa & Major Credit Cards
Open Daily • Lunch & Dinner

General Manager
KATE O'REILLY KNOX

Chef
RENZO VERONESE

Recommended Items

Appetizers

MEZZELUNE FILLED WITH
WHITE BEANS, BASIL &
PARMESAN, SAUTÉED SHRIMP

• MARINATED EGGPLANT FILLED
WITH GOAT CHEESE WITH
OVEN-CURED TOMATOES
& BASIL OIL

Entrées

CALABRIAN-STYLE
SPAGHETTI WITH ANCHOVY,
ORANGE, GARLIC, BLACK
OLIVES, MINT & CHILE FLAKES

• OAKWOOD-ROASTED CHICKEN
WITH ROSEMARY, POTATOES &
SEASONAL VEGETABLES

WITH WHITE WALLS BRIGHTENED BY WHIMSICAL MURALS OF vegetables and Italian plates ("piatti"), terracotta tiles on the floors and counters, and a rustic open kitchen, Piatti is perfect for long, relaxed meals in the company of friends. Located in the heart of Yountville, the cheerful restaurant serves vibrant and flavorful regional Italian dishes that are simple yet innovative. The good food and superb service keep guests coming back for more. Most popular are the restaurant's wood-fired pizza and rotisserie-roasted meats and poultry and, of course, the pasta. ♦ Piatti's romantic outdoor patio is relaxed and gracious, perfect for sipping a glass of the restaurant's large selection of California or Italian wine. All in all, Piatti's lighthearted atmosphere perfectly captures both the Italian spirit and the wine country region's unique style and flair.

AVERAGE DINNER FOR TWO: $45
DOES NOT INCLUDE WINE, TAX AND GRATUITY

THE RESTAURANT

AT MEADOWOOD
900 MEADOWOOD LANE
ST. HELENA, CA 94574
(707) 963-3646

Visa & Major Credit Cards
Dinner Daily • Sunday Brunch

General Manager
JORG LIPPUNER

Chef
ROY BREIMAN

Recommended Items

Appetizers
SEARED FLORIDA RED SNAPPER
W/FENNEL, ARTICHOKES & DILL
• ROAST LANGOUSTINES W/FOIE
GRAS & TRUFFLE OIL • WARM
SALAD OF ROAST SQUAB
W/LENTILS & MIXED GREENS

Entrées
MAINE LOBSTER W/YOUNG
LEEKS, CABERNET &
CARAMELIZED FIGS • ROAST RAB-
BIT SERVED WITH SMOKED
BACON & CREAMY TRUFFLED
POLENTA • ROUGET "NIÇOISE"
W/CAPERS, BLACK OLIVES,
TOMATO FONDUE & FRIED BASIL

NESTLED IN ITS OWN SMALL VALLEY AT THE END OF A COUNTRY lane, Meadowood is just off the Silverado Trail, minutes outside St. Helena. Yet this beautiful resort is so secluded and luxurious that visitors immediately feel miles away from the rest of the world. Located on the upper level of the clubhouse, The Restaurant's interior and large decks overlook the immaculate golf course, croquet lawns and the wooded hills beyond. ♦ A native Californian, Chef Roy Breiman has worked with great chefs in New York and Los Angeles, and recently completed a stint at the Hotel Negresco in Nice, France. He is excited about sharing his lifelong passion for Provençal cuisine with the Napa Valley. "I believe in this style of cooking because of its purity, simplicity and the respect for natural flavors that it encourages." Certainly the surrounding beauty of Meadowood is in sync with Roy's inspiration. ♦ Meadowood's Wine Cellar, selected by the renowned wine expert Bob Thureen, holds wines from practically every Napa Valley producer, approaching 300 now. Many of the labels are rarely seen outside Northern California.

AVERAGE DINNER FOR TWO: $85
DOES NOT INCLUDE WINE, TAX AND GRATUITY

SHOWLEY'S

1327 RAILROAD AVENUE
ST. HELENA, CA 94574
(707) 963-1200

Visa & Major Credit Cards
Closed Monday • Lunch & Dinner

Manager/Proprietor	*Chef/Proprietors*
ALLISON LANE SIMPSON	GRANT W. SHOWLEY
Proprietor	SHARON W. SHOWLEY
CLARK SIMPSON	

Recommended Items

Appetizers

GRILLED JAPANESE EGGPLANT ON A BED OF CARAMELIZED ONIONS, CAPERS, TOMATO CONFIT & PESTO • FRISÉE SALAD WITH GRILLED PEAR, CHEVRE, PANCETTA & GARLIC DRESSING

Entrées

ROASTED MONKFISH FILLET, COATED WITH CHESTNUT FLOUR WITH PINOT NOIR BUTTER SAUCE & GARLIC MASHED POTATOES • BRAISED DUCK WITH GARLIC MASHED POTATOES, HOUSE MADE CHUTNEY ROSEMARY-PINOT NOIR GLAZE

LOCATED ONE BLOCK EAST OF MAIN STREET IN DOWNTOWN ST. Helena, Showley's serves California cuisine with strong French and Italian influences. From patés to ice cream, everything is made in-house using the superb local ingredients readily available to the kitchen. ♦ The building dates back to 1858. Then it was a gracious and restorative haven for the weary traveler; now it is also a place that excites the culinary adventurer. In summer, the courtyard with its hundred-year-old fig tree is one of the most coveted places to dine in the Napa Valley. Boasts Allison Simpson, "It has been the scene of countless marriage proposals." When in season, figs from this magnificent tree are actually used in several innovative menu choices. ♦ You know a restaurant is special when you have a tough time deciding what to order because everything is so wonderful. Locals have been overheard referring to Showley's as "Napa Valley's best kept secret." Whatever you order and whenever you dine at Showley's, prepare to be seduced.

AVERAGE DINNER FOR TWO: $45
DOES NOT INCLUDE WINE, TAX AND GRATUITY

TERRA

1345 RAILROAD AVENUE
ST. HELENA, CA 94574
(707) 963-8931

Visa, MasterCard, Diners & Carte Blan Only
Closed Tuesday • Dinner Only

Proprietor
LISSA DOUMANI

Chef/Proprietor
HIROYOSHI SONE

Recommended Items

Appetizers
FRESH MIYAGI OYSTERS
IN PONZU SAUCE
WITH DAIKON RADISH
• SOUP PISTOU WITH
RAVIOLI OF GOAT CHEESE
• CROQUETTE OF DUCK CONFIT
WITH WILD MUSHROOM SALAD

Entrées
GRILLED FILET OF SALMON
WITH THAI RED CURRY SAUCE
& BASMATI RICE • GRILLED
WOLF RANCH QUAIL WITH
PITHIVIER OF FOIE GRAS &
MUSHROOM • ACQUA PAZZA

HIROYOSHI SONE, A GRADUATE OF OSAKA'S TSUJI COOKING SCHOOL, and Lissa Doumani, whose parents own Stag's Leap Winery, met in Los Angeles in 1983 at Spago, where Hiro was sous chef and Lissa was second pastry chef. After opening Spago in Tokyo for Wolfgang Puck in 1984, Hiro became head chef at Spago/Los Angeles until he left in 1988. ♦ "Hiro said on national television that his dream was to own a restaurant in the wine country," says Lissa with a laugh, "so we had to come here and do this!" ♦ Her warm good humor and Sone's free-wheeling cooking style found their niche in St. Helena's historic Hatchery Building. Built in 1884, its fieldstone walls, high ceilings and exposed wood beams share the welcoming simplicity of Terra's owners. "We wanted the kind of place where if you drop your fork, you don't feel bad," explains Lissa, "but where you can hear yourself talk." ♦ One topic of conversation is always the food. Chef Hiro's refined amalgam of French, Italian, Japanese and Chinese cuisines puts Terra at the top of Napa Valley's exciting restaurants.

AVERAGE DINNER FOR TWO: $60
DOES NOT INCLUDE WINE, TAX AND GRATUITY

Tra Vigne

1050 Charter Oak
AT HIGHWAY 29
St. Helena, Ca 94574
(707) 963-4444

Visa & Major Credit Cards
Open Daily • Lunch & Dinner

Proprietor	Chef
Kevin Cronin	Michael Chiarello

Recommended Items

Appetizers

WARM SALAD OF SPRING GREENS, GOAT CHEESE, & PANCHETTA DRESSING, PORT SOAKED SOUR CHERRIES • OVEN-ROASTED POLENTA W/WILD MUSHROOMS

Entrées

SMOKED & BRAISED "NIMAN-SCHELL" BEEF SHORT RIBS W/GARLIC SOFT POLENTA, NATURAL BROTH • TUBE-SHAPED PASTA FROM "RUSTICHELLA D'ABRUZZO" W/A SEASONAL VARIETY OF SEAFOOD

THE WILDLY SUCCESSFUL PEOPLE AT REAL RESTAURANTS PUT their Midas touch on yet another popular eatery. Located in a landmark stone building, Tra Vigne is Napa Valley's current favorite, attracting an animated crowd of locals and visitors day and night. ♦ The cuisine is what Michael Chiarello likes to call "American food prepared with the heart, hands and eyes of an Italian." Everything is made on the premises – prosciutto, cheeses, breads, pastas, gelati – from ultra-fresh local ingredients. For fans who want to prolong their pleasure, the restaurant's Cantinetta offers many of these delicacies for takeout. ♦ The decor packs a striking visual punch. Talented designer Michael Guthrie has created a neo-Gothic feel, with gilt and modern accents softened by such rustic touches as ash tables and rush-seated chairs. The vine-covered brick courtyard provides a tranquil alternative to the action inside.

AVERAGE DINNER FOR TWO: $50
DOES NOT INCLUDE WINE, TAX AND GRATUITY

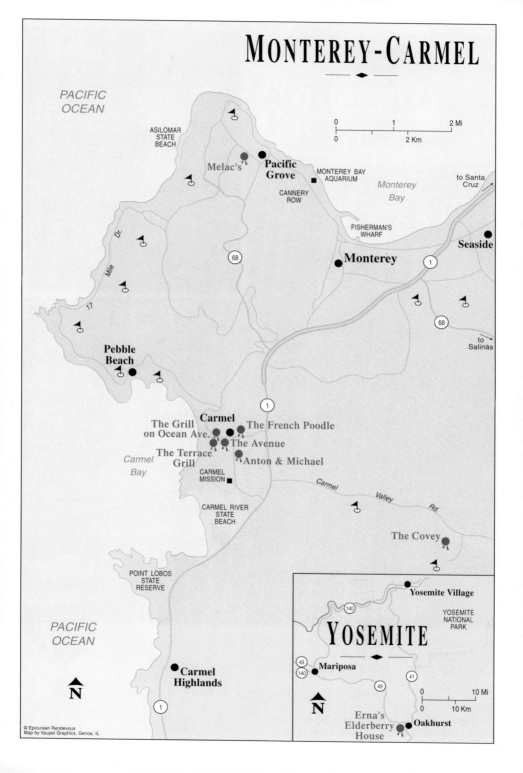

MONTEREY-CARMEL

PACIFIC
OCEAN

ASILOMAR
STATE
BEACH

Melac's

**Pacific
Grove**

MONTEREY BAY
AQUARIUM

CANNERY
ROW

*Monterey
Bay*

to Santa
Cruz

FISHERMAN'S
WHARF

Monterey

Seaside

68

17 Mile Dr.

**Pebble
Beach**

68

to
Salinas

1

Carmel

The Grill
on Ocean Ave.

The French Poodle

The Avenue

*Carmel
Bay*

The Terrace
Grill

Anton & Michael

CARMEL
MISSION

Carmel   *Valley*   *Rd.*

CARMEL RIVER
STATE
BEACH

The Covey

POINT LOBOS
STATE
RESERVE

PACIFIC
OCEAN

**Carmel
Highlands**

1

N

© Epicurean Rendevous
Map by Vaupel Graphics, Genoa, IL

0   1   2 Mi
0   2 Km

Yosemite Village

YOSEMITE
NATIONAL
PARK

140

YOSEMITE

49

Mariposa

140

49

41

Erna's
Elderberry
House

Oakhurst

0   10 Mi
0   10 Km

N

QUAIL LODGE
RESORT & GOLF CLUB
CARMEL, CALIFORNIA

ANTON & MICHEL

MISSION
BETWEEN OCEAN & 7TH
CARMEL, CA 93921
(408) 624-2406

Visa & Major Credit Cards
Open Daily • Lunch & Dinner

Proprietor
ANTON SALAMEH
General Manager
BERT SIMPSON

Executive Chef
MAX MURAMATSU

Recommended Items

Appetizers
ESCARGOTS WITH GARLIC-
CREAM SAUCE • SCAMPII-STYLE
PRAWNS WITH GARLIC BUTTER,
TOMATO, GREEN ONION &
FRESH HERBS • MONTEREY BAY
ABALONE

Entrées
MEDALLIONS OF VEAL WITH
SAUTÉED SPINACH & MADEIRA
WINE SAUCE • PRAWNS &
SCALLOPS FRICASSÉE WITH
BOUILLABAISSE CREAM SAUCE,
SERVED WITH PUFF PASTRY
SHELL • RACK OF LAMB AU JUS,
HERB-DIJON MUSTARD, CARVED
TABLESIDE

FOR A REFRESHING DOSE OF OLD-FASHIONED ROMANCE, ANTON & Michel is the place to dine. Its pretty interior of pink walls trimmed in cream, impressionistic oil paintings, stately columns and soft candlelight is flattering and elegant. Huge windows frame a view of Carmel's Court of the Fountains and its beautiful reflecting pool, with outdoor tables for lunch *al fresco*. A cozy lounge makes pre-dinner drinks a pleasure, and a semi-private room offers the warmth of a fireplace. ♦ Owner Anton Salameh is usually on hand to make sure every patron is treated like a V.I.P. He need not worry: Anton & Michel is justly renowned for its exceptional service. Where else can you find at least four classic desserts prepared tableside, from bananas flambé to exquisite cherries jubilee? Or Caesar salad tossed and dressed while you watch? ♦ Excellent steak, veal and lamb, as well as fresh Monterey Bay seafood, highlight the menu, with a Wine Spectator Award-winning wine list that emphasizes California red varietals. As one would expect, the after-dinner drink selection also is too impressive to ignore. And what better way to prolong the pleasure of dining at Anton & Michel.

AVERAGE DINNER FOR TWO: $70
DOES NOT INCLUDE WINE, TAX AND GRATUITY

NEW AMERICAN

THE AVENUE

OCEAN AVENUE
BETWEEN LINCOLN AND MONTE VERDE
CARMEL, CA 93921
(408) 624-4395

Visa & Major Credit Cards
Open Daily • Lunch & Dinner

Proprietor
JACK HAKIM

Proprietor
NEDJ KASHFI

Recommended Items

Appetizers
AHI TUNA CARPACCHIO,
CRUSHED PEPPERCORN CRUST,
HERBED BABY GREENS &
SESAME AIOLI • DUNGENESS
CRAB & SCALLION CAKES, AILEN-
TRE CHILE SAUCE, BABY GREENS
& MARINATED TOMATOES

Entreès
GRILLED CHILEAN SEA BASS, WARM
TABOULI, SAUTEED PEPPERS &
POMEGRANATE CITRUS
VINAIGRETTE • ROSEMARY
GRILLED LAMB SIRLOIN, WARM
SPINACH & WILD MUSHROOM
SALAD, OVEN DRIED TOMATOES
& CRISPY ONIONS

FROM THE MOMENT YOU WALK THROUGH THE ARCHED DOOR and step onto the beautiful flagstone floor you are swept up and transported into a warm, gracious and indulgent cocoon. There are two beautifully appointed and intimate dining rooms, one with a fireplace and a staircase that charmingly leads nowhere except maybe to heaven. All this as well as an abundance of flowers and the outside garden gives you a mediterranean feel, as though you might be in the south of France. ♦ The gracious and sumptuous atmosphere is every bit equaled by Avenue's "New American" cuisine. The braised veal osso bucco with smoked bacon polenta, caramelized onion and roasted garlic sauce are significant and flawlessly prepared dishes. Desserts are different variations of delicious opulence. The caramelized banana and chocolate bread pudding is the perfect way to end a perfect evening.

AVERAGE DINNER FOR TWO: $50
DOES NOT INCLUDE WINE, TAX AND GRATUITY

THE COVEY

8205 VALLEY GREENS DRIVE
QUAIL LODGE RESORT & GOLF CLUB
CARMEL, CA 93923
(408) 624-1581

Visa & Major Credit Cards
Open Daily • Dinner Only

General Manager
CSABA AJAN

Executive Chef
BOB WILLIAMSON

Recommended Items

Appetizers
BELUGA CAVIAR
• SHRIMP & SCALLOP QUENELLE
• MAINE LOBSTER SALAD

Entrées
SANTA BARBARA ABALONE
• BREAST OF PHEASANT WITH
DRIED MICHIGAN CHERRIES &
SHIITAKE MUSHROOMS
• GOLDEN GARLIC SCAMPI
• A VARIETY OF
SPA CUISINE DISHES

EXQUISITE CUISINE WITH A REFINED EUROPEAN FLAIR IN A country club atmosphere — it's all yours at Quail Lodge in Carmel, where the undulating Carmel River meanders around a golf course and ten picturesque lakes. ♦ The Covey restaurant's natural wood interiors give it a warm, homey feeling, while its large glass windows and skylights bring in the beauty of the outdoors. ♦ The Covey presents an à la carte menu that reflects Chef Bob Williamson's classical training in Switzerland. His European touch is leavened with a distinctively American style, the result of years spent in Oregon, Chicago and Canada and the availability of California's abundant year-round garden harvests. ♦ Here, sauces are light, the vegetables are al dente and the garnishes feature the artichokes of the Monterey Peninsula. The wine list features a superb selection of hard-to-find California wines.

AVERAGE DINNER FOR TWO: $70
DOES NOT INCLUDE WINE, TAX AND GRATUITY

THE FRENCH POODLE

JUNIPERO & FIFTH AVENUE
CARMEL, CA 93921
(408) 624-8643

Visa & Major Credit Cards
Closed Sunday & Wednesday • Dinner Only

Cellar Master
RICHARD VEDRINES
Proprietor
MICHELE VEDRINES

Chef/Proprietor
MARC VEDRINES

Recommended Items

Appetizers
DUNGENESS CRAB LEGS
WITH CHAMPAGNE SAUCE,
SEASONED WITH SAFFRON &
CAVIAR • CHICKEN &
DUCK LIVER MOUSSE

Entrées
GRILLED SLICED BREAST OF
DUCK IN OLD PORT WINE
SAUCE • LOIN OF CALIFORNIA
LAMB SAUTÉED WITH
SCALLOPED POTATOES
• ABALONE MEUNIÈRE

AFTER ALMOST THREE DECADES IN CARMEL, THE FRENCH POODLE remains as vital as the day it was opened by Marc and Michèle Vedrines. With Michèle overseeing every detail, from the selection of classical music and individually lit paintings to the elegant remodeling in muted tones of raspberry with black, it has the intimate appeal of a beloved friend. ♦ Chef Marc Vedrines has cooked for such famous people as Charles de Gaulle, Gerald Ford and Clint Eastwood, yet he is as modest as his wife is outgoing. A follower of Escoffier who spent eight years as chef at The Lodge in Pebble Beach, Chef Vedrines presents the masterpieces of French cuisine. Authentic and remarkably consistent, his dishes have earned The French Poodle its reputation as the Carmel restaurant French people most love and respect. ♦ An excellent wine list leans toward France, and on hand to help diners make the right selection is another talented Vedrines, son Richard. Like his parents, he brings a strong sense of family pride to what has become a Carmel treasure.

AVERAGE DINNER FOR TWO: $60
DOES NOT INCLUDE WINE, TAX AND GRATUITY

VIP

THE GRILL ON OCEAN AVENUE

OCEAN AVENUE
BETWEEN DOLORES & LINCOLN
CARMEL, CA 93921
(408) 624-2569

Visa & Major Credit Cards
Open Daily • Lunch & Dinner

Proprietor
ANTON M. SALAMEH
General Manager
BRIAN J. CULLEN

Executive Chef
HISAYUKI "MAX"
MURAMATSU

Recommended Items
♦♦

Appetizers
OAK-GRILLED CALAMARI WITH
KAIWARE, SHISO & SOY-SHALLOT
VINAIGRETTE • DUNGENESS
CRAB CAKES WITH LEMON-
CAPER BEURRE BLANC • WARM
GOAT CHEESE COATED WITH
ROASTED WALNUTS & A TOMA-
TO-BASIL SAUCE

Entrées
DUCK RAVIOLI: BLACK PEPPER
PASTA FILLED WITH TENDER
DUCK & MUSHROOM MOUSSE IN
AN ORANGE BEURRE BLANC
• OAK-GRILLED SALMON WITH
OKRA, SWEET POTATO TEMPURA
& WASABI-CILANTRO
BEURRE BLANC

ON CARMEL'S BUSIEST TOURIST STREET, THE GRILL ON OCEAN Avenue is a refuge of calm and fine dining. Flower boxes beneath three lovely arched windows beckon strollers into an airy mission-style room, with a stone fireplace on one side and a bar on the other. A tapestry-covered banquette runs along one wall, with bold black-framed paintings above it, and roomy booths anchor the center of the dining area. The atmosphere is comfortable, casual and very Carmel. ♦ The cuisine of Chef Max Muramatsu is a subtle blend of Japanese, French and California flavors: classically executed, generously portioned and expertly sauced. Trained at Maxim's in Paris, he was twice named best chef in Tokyo. His rack of lamb, pink, tender morsels buttressed by an irresistible mound of garlic mashed potatoes, is state-of-the-art. ♦ A medium-sized wine list is strong on local selections, giving diners a chance to sample some of Monterey County's rising stars. As for dessert, the baked pear strudel and apple-blueberry tart are not to be missed. But don't take our word for it, ask the waiters. You won't find a friendlier staff in all of Carmel.

AVERAGE DINNER FOR TWO: $50
DOES NOT INCLUDE WINE, TAX AND GRATUITY

MELAC'S

663 LIGHTHOUSE AVENUE
PACIFIC GROVE, CA 93950
(408) 375-1743

Visa & Major Credit Cards
Dinner Tues-Sun • Lunch Tues-Fri

Proprietor
JACQUES MELAC

Chef/Proprietor
JANET MELAC

Recommended Items

Appetizers
ROQUEFORT TIMBAL WITH BABY LETTTUCES & HAZELNUT VINAIGRETTE • GRILLED QUAIL WITH ROASTED GARLIC, FRESH HERBS & OREGON CHANTERELLES

Entrées
SEAFOOD CASSOULET • MEDALLIONS OF VEAL WITH MADEIRA WINE & LEMON CONFIT • ROASTED DUCKLING WITH PORT & FRESH FIGS

LIKE A WARM COUNTRY RESTAURANT, MELAC'S SACRIFICES GLAMour for the glory of French cuisine. This cozy restaurant is filled with the dedication and friendliness of its owners, Jacques and Janet Melac. But the husband-wife theme has an interesting twist: American-born Janet is the chef, while French-born Jacques is the man up front. ♦ The two met in Paris where Janet graduated first in her class at the Cordon Bleu School and apprenticed with Gérard Pangaud at the Michelin two-star Boulogne Billancourt. Both worked with Gaston Lenôtre in Paris and later in Texas. Janet cooks every dish to order and changes the menu daily to make use of the freshest seasonal products. Framed by several crisp vegetables, her dishes are generously portioned and attractively presented. ♦ Jacques is a gracious and sensitive host who loves to help patrons pair wine with his wife's creations. He tastes every wine before including it on his list, balancing the best of California's small wineries with classic French selections.

AVERAGE DINNER FOR TWO: $60
DOES NOT INCLUDE WINE, TAX AND GRATUITY

VIP

CALIFORNIA/INTERNATIONAL

THE TERRACE GRILL

LA PLAYA HOTEL
EIGHTH AVENUE & CAMINO REAL
CARMEL, CA 93921
(408) 624-4010

Visa & Major Credit Cards
Open Daily • Breakfast, Lunch & Dinner • Sunday Brunch

General Manager
TOM GLIDDEN

Chef de Cuisine
BUNYAN FORTUNE
Sous Chef
WILLIAM DAVID SMITH

Recommended Items

Appetizers
GRILLED BUFFALO QUESADILLA
• DUNGENESS CRABCAKES
OVER A FENNEL RATATOUILLE
& CORN RELISH

Entrées
GRILLED FILET MIGNON WITH
PORTABELLO MUSHROOMS
& PINOT NOIR SAUCE
• HERB & PEPPERCORN
CRUSTED SWORDFISH
WITH A SWEET
PEPPER HOLLANDAISE

BUILT IN 1904 AS AN ARTIST'S MANSION, THE MISSION-STYLE LA Playa Hotel evokes the atmosphere and hospitality of Old Carmel. The elegant Terrace Grill has a view of the ocean on one side and immaculate flower gardens on the other, with an adjacent terrace perfect for breakfast or lunch on a sunny day. When the fog rolls in, guests seek warmth in a cozy, wood-paneled bar. ♦ Executive Chef Bunyan Fortune comes to La Playa by way of the nearby Highlands Inn and Lodge at Pebble Beach. Trained in classic French technique at the National Cooking Institute in Denver, Bunyan believes in keeping guests happy. "There is no right or wrong; the only thing that matters is customer satisfaction." He continues, "Food is constantly evolving through communication with other lands, and blending new ideas with familiar ingredients is very exciting to me."

AVERAGE DINNER FOR TWO: $45
DOES NOT INCLUDE WINE, TAX AND GRATUITY

ERNA'S ELDERBERRY HOUSE

48688 VICTORIA LANE
OFF HIGHWAY 41
OAKHURST, CA 93644
(209) 683-6800

Visa & MasterCard Only
Dinner Wed-Mon • Lunch Wed-Fri • Sunday Brunch

Sommelier	*Chef/Proprietor*
RENÉE-NICOLE KUBIN	ERNA KUBIN-CLANIN

Recommended Items

Appetizers
YOUNG LETTUCES WITH FRUIT
VINAIGRETTE • GRILLED
SHRIMP, SCALLOPS WITH ROE
ATTACHED & CRABCAKES, WITH
CILANTRO-CUCUMBER SAUCE

Entrées
ROASTED VEAL MEDALLIONS ON
FENNEL, PERNOD SAUCE &
PEAR CHUTNEY • NUTTED
WILD RICE & SIX SEASONAL
VEGETABLES

"ONE OF THE MOST ELEGANT AND STYLISH RESTAURANTS IN THE nation is a little-known place nestled in the foothills of the Sierra Nevada ..." With those words in *The New York Times* of July 8, 1987, Craig Claiborne began a paean to Erna's Elderberry House that brought its classic French cuisine to the attention of serious gourmets. Since then, *Gourmet, Bon Appetit* and countless other publications have discovered Vienna-born Erna Kubin-Clanin's romantic hideaway just outside of Yosemite. ♦ Built of stone and surrounded by oaks, pines and elderberry bushes, the restaurant has two country-style dining rooms, three private rooms, a natural stone bar and an outdoor terrace. Every detail, from the French fabrics to the antique buffets, is exquisite, chosen by Erna with the same love and care she brings to her six-course, prix-fixe dinners and her *Wine Spectator* award-winning wine list. ♦ Like Craig Claiborne, who came for dinner and stayed three days, guests who wish to prolong the magic can stay at the enchanting Château du Sureau, Erna's nine-room castle hotel.

SIX COURSE PRIX-FIXE DINNER FOR TWO: $116
DOES NOT INCLUDE WINE, TAX AND GRATUITY

VIP

WORLD CLASS WINES

BY NORMAN ROBY

AS THE 1990s UNFOLD, THE QUALITY OF wine throughout the world has never been higher. Beginning in the 1960s, California upstarts challenged the French and Italian wine industries. Other states and other countries soon followed. After a decade of growth and exper-imentation in the 1970s, wines took a quantum leap as an international spirit of cooperation began. ◆ Today, winemakers from France, Italy and the United States regularly visit each other's cellars to exchange information and to collaborate on research projects. Without compromising the integrity of their own distinctive wine regions, they have created new approaches to grape growing and winemaking. The result: better wines and more choices than ever before.

WINE TALK

PART OF THE ENJOYMENT OF WINES comes from the conversations they inspire. Quite often the subject is the wine itself. Talking about wine should be easy and relaxed. To help matters along, we have defined the most commonly used words and phrases, with particular emphasis on wine aromas. Most wine commentary proceeds by analogies and suggestions, so trust your instincts, offer your impressions and create descriptions.

◆ AROMA All-purpose word for the smell of a wine, which may vary in type (fruity, floral, spicy) and in strength. Aroma is used in the general sense and is usually positive.

◆ ASTRINGENT The sensation of a wine that leaves a puckery feel in the mouth and seems to dry out the palate. Most young Cabernets and Zinfan-dels are astringent. Tannins, from the grapes and oak barrels, contribute to astringency, which is more common in red wines.

VICHON
CALIFORNIA

**Winery Of The Year
Two Years In A Row**
*Wine & Spirits
Magazine*

♦ AUSTERE Characteristic of wines that are lean in body and high in acidity but overall on the pleasant side. Usually white wines are likely to be austere in style.

♦ BALANCED When all of a wine's components (fruit, alcohol, acidity, tannin, oak, sweetness) exist in a harmonious way, the wine is said to be balanced.

♦ BERRYLIKE Common aroma description for wines with a fairly distinct fruit character. Zinfandels are often similar to blackberries, Cabernets to black currants and Pinot Noirs to cherries.

♦ BODY The relative weight of a wine or its viscosity. Ranges from thin to light, to medium, to full-bodied. How a wine clings to the sides of a glass when you swirl it is an indication of its body.

♦ BOUQUET The odors developed through the aging process as distinguished from the fruity/spicy aroma of the grape.

♦ COMPLEX Describes both aromas and flavors, and the existence of several facets simultaneously. Multidimensional wines are complex. The opposite style is simple or one-dimensional.

♦ CRISP Wines that are lively on the palate and leave you with a lip-smacking impression similar to tart. Usually results from relatively high acidity.

♦ DRY Basically, the opposite of sweet.

♦ EARTHY Exists in varying degrees, from a subtle aroma of dusty weediness to a pungent aroma of mushrooms and truffles. More commonly found in red wines.

♦ FLORAL Aromas similar to flowers in bloom are said to be floral. White wines such as Johannisberg Riesling and Gewurztraminer are often floral with hints of jasmine and orange blossom. The aroma of violets and roses exists in some Pinot Noirs.

♦ GRASSY A fresh, lively aroma reminiscent of freshly cut grass, usually considered pleasant, and characteristic of many Sauvignon Blancs. Some Chardonnays and a few Chenin Blancs can be grassy.

♦ HERBACEOUS/HERBAL Collective terms for aromas hinting of dried herbs such as sage, dill and mint. Herbaceousness is most often found in Sauvignon Blanc.

♦ HONEY An enticing sweet smell present in some white wines. It is usually a result of *Botrytis cinerea,* "the noble rot."

♦ NOSE The combination of all odors, aroma, bouquet, oak, etc., detected by the olfactory sense.

♦ OAKED The aroma derived directly from oak barrel aging and usually described as vanillalike. The oak is fired to conform to the barrel shape.

♦ SMOKY An aroma derived mostly from fired oak barrels and often perceived as toasty or roasted, similar to the smell of burning leaves.

♦ SPICY Many fine wines are characteristically spicy, suggesting cloves, cinnamon and pepper. Zinfandel and Syrah wines tend to be peppery; among white wines, Gewurztraminer can be very spicy.

♦ SUPPLE A wine that is extremely subtle in a soft, smooth style without being heavy in body.

♦ VEGETATIVE This covers a range of aromas, from the quite attractive smell of green olives and bell peppers often common to Cabernet Sauvignon and Sauvignon Blanc, to the less attractive green bean and asparagus smells sometimes detected in both types of wine.

♦ YEASTY An aroma similar to fresh-baked bread, highly desirable in Champagne and sparkling wines. Some white wines, notably Chardonnay and Sauvignon Blanc, are aged in contact with yeasty and acquire a subtle yeastiness. ■

A

CENTURY

OF

STYLE

AND

INNOVATION

Simi Winery   Healdsburg   Sonoma County   California

Jordan

 LEGANCE IN A BOTTLE

JORDAN VINEYARDS
PO BOX 878
HEALDSBURG, CALIFORNIA
95448

707 431 5250

THE BEST OF
CALIFORNIA WINES

By Norman Roby

*C*alifornia wines have definitely come of age. The finest are now being collected, coveted and cellared with the zeal once reserved for prestigious European wines. Perhaps even more telling is the way the trendsetting restaurants of today, which once may have offered nothing but French wines, proudly offer an array of California wines. European wine producers have bestowed the ultimate compliment on California as a prime wine region by choosing to become a part of the excitement. Companies such as Möet et Chandon, Piper, Pommery, Roederer, Mouton-Rothschild, Taittinger, G.H. Mumm, Freixenet and many others have joined the dynamic California wine world.

With more than 800 wineries in existence and others on the way, no winery will be able to rest on its laurels. As good as California wines are today, the overall quality level will only continue to rise.

CALIFORNIA
VITICULTURAL AREAS

NORTH COAST
NAPA VALLEY
SONOMA VALLEY
Sacramento
San Francisco
SIERRA FOOTHILLS
CENTRAL COAST
Los Angeles
TEMECULA
San Diego

VITICULTURAL AREAS

OF INTEREST TO MOST WINE CONSUMERS is where the grapes were grown — in other words, the wine's origin. By January of 1983 the Treasury Department's Bureau of Alcohol, Tobacco and Firearms tightened the regulations governing place names. The growing region must be defined in terms of boundaries approved by the BATF. Now, when a name like Alexander Valley is used, at least 85 percent of the wine comes from that growing region. However, the winery itself does not have to be located within that region. When the name of a county appears, at least 75 percent of the wine must originate in that county.

Far Niente

The Napa Valley Wine Estate

1995

Estate Winery
of the Year

Wine & Spirits November 1994

♦ *California* Still commonly used by both small and large producers, this designation means 100 percent of the wine came from California.

♦ *Napa Valley* Running thirty miles in length, this famous wine region keeps on getting bigger and better. Today, with close to 35,000 acres and about 200 wineries, Napa Valley is the leader in wine quality and innovation.

♦ *Rutherford Bench* Called benchlands, the naturally terraced, iron-rich slopes between Oakville and Rutherford comprise the heart of Cabernet country.

♦ *Carneros District* One of the most visible viticultural areas, the Carneros District falls within both Napa and Sonoma counties. Close to San Francisco Bay, it is a cool growing area producing exquisite grapes. The region is becoming well known for its Pinot Noir and Chardonnay.

♦ *Russian River Valley* This viticultural area follows the course of the Russian River and thus varies widely in its climate. The lower sector is a cool area preferred for its Chardonnay, Pinot Noir and sparkling wine varieties.

♦ *Alexander Valley* Located in the inland northeast corner of Sonoma County, the Alexander Valley is large (12,000 acres) and relatively warm. It is quite versatile and reputed for rich Chardonnays and sought-after Cabernet Sauvignons.

♦ *Sonoma Valley* Still known as the Valley of the Moon, this historic 5,000-acre region falls on the southwestern side of the Mayacamas mountain range, which separates it from the Napa Valley.

♦ *North Coast* This covers a wide range of vineyards in such diverse counties as Napa, Sonoma, Mendocino, Lake, Marin and Solano.

♦ *Central Coast* A large viticultural area, the Central Coast includes vineyards in the counties of Monterey, Santa Barbara, San Luis Obispo and San Benito.

♦ *Sierra Foothills* Another multi-county place name, Sierra Foothills includes the historic Gold Rush regions of El Dorado, Amador, Yuba and Calaveras counties.

♦ *Temecula* Located between San Diego and Riverside County, this viticultural area is tempered by cool breezes and seems to excel in white varietals.

SPARKLING WINES

Although technically only French sparkling wines can be called champagnes, some California producers do use the term. Either way, California now makes millions of bottles of this delicious bubbly wine, ready to be enjoyed on any occasion. The finest are produced by the Methode Champenoise, the traditional, labor-intensive system required of all French Champagnes. Labor-saving methods generally result in less satisfying flavors. The combination of fruitiness and yeastiness characteristic of California sparkling wines gives them a more youthful style than those from France. Among the best: Domaine Chandon, Napa Mumm, Gloria Ferrer, Iron Horse Vineyards, Roederer Estate, Maison Deutz, Piper-Sonoma, Schramsberg Vineyards; "J" and Scharffenberger.

CHARDONNAY

Chardonnay is without question the richest and most complex-tasting wine. Since the early 1970s, when California chardonnays began attracting international recognition, the number of first-rate Chardonnays has increased dramatically. The prevailing character of chardonnay is a spiced apple, ripe apricot aroma in a medium-bodied to medium-full-bodied style. The subtle individual differences in style depend upon the degree of oak-aging and regional character imposed by the climate and soil. Some of the top names are: Matanzas Creek Winery, Grgich Hills Cellars, DeLoach Vineyards, Chateau Montelena, Acacia Winery, Chalone, Far Niente Winery, Kistler Vineyards, Trefethen Vineyards, Sonoma Cutter, and Cosentino's The Sculptor.

SAUVIGNON BLANC & OTHER WHITES

The second most popular white wine today, Sauvignon Blanc/Fumé Blanc is a bright fruity wine

DE LOACH VINEYARDS
20
Years of Excellence

1791 Olivet Road
Santa Rosa, CA 95401
(707) 526-9111

Château St. Jean

ONLY THE FINEST.

Château St. Jean

CINQ C
Cabernet S
SONOMA
199

Château St. Jean
ROBERT YOUNG VINEYARDS
1993
Chardonnay
ALEXANDER VALLEY

with an aroma of melon and fresh grass; the wine is usually medium bodied with a hint of oak. Among the most representative are Fumé Blanc from Robert Mondavi, and Ferrari Carano, and Sauvignon Blanc from Cakebread Cellars, Matanzas Creek, Duckhorn, and Silverado Vineyards. Somewhat lighter in body and character, Chenin Blanc remains a pleasing, versatile white; the most pleasant version are make by Pine Ridge, Simi and Chappellet. Semillon, less well-known, offers a wonderful treat with its fig-like aroma and rich flavors. Signorello makes a beauty. The spice and floral character of Gewurztraminer offers itself as yet another taste possibility, and one of the best around these days is Beringer Vineyard's Gewurztraminer.

PINOT NOIR

Pinot Noir has come a long way in recent years, then again this red varietal wine had plenty of room for improvement. Only winemakers interested in Pinot Noir located the ideal sites for growing this temperamental grape. Textbook Pinot Noir capture a spicy cinnamon and wild-cherry aroma and offer a smooth-as-satin texture. The color tends to be lighter than most red wines and may even show a brown tint. Carneros District (located in both Napa and Sonoma counties), Russian River Valley, Monterey and Sonoma Valley are the premier appellations. The stars are: Dehlinger Winery, Acacia Winery, Calera Wines, Saintsbury Cellars, Chalone Vineyards, Carneros Creek Winery, Signorello, Navarro Vineyards and Beaulieu.

MERLOT

The greatest success story of the late 1980s, Merlot has emerged from relative obscurity to rival Cabernet Sauvignon as the preferred full-flavored red wine. The Louis M. Martini winery made California's first varietal Merlot in 1968; Sterling vineyards made the second in 1969. Now every winery with access to Merlot grapes produces one. Merlot's central appeal resides in aromas similar to Cabernet—black currants, black cherries and herbs—but with a softness and smoothness all its own. Among the best are: Cosentino Winery, Duckhorn Vineyards, Matanzas Creek Winery, Cuvaison Winery, Franciscan Vineyards, Markham Vineyards, St. Francis Winery, Newton and St. Clement.

CABERNET SAUVIGNON

Outstanding Cabernet Sauvignons have come from California vineyards for many decades. In the 1940s and 1950s, the leaders were Beaulieu, Inglenook, Charles Krug and Louis Martini. Today, over 400 wineries offer this red varietal in a range of styles and prices. Sonoma County and Napa Valley are home to the majority of the top-ranked California Cabernets. Some wineries make full-bodied versions with youthful tannins, which age slowly. More are aiming for refined fruity flavors, herbaceous character and early maturity. As winemakers have become more skilled at their trade, they are using blenders such as Cabernet Franc and/or Merlot when they feel a more exciting wine will result, first class ones include: Caymus Vineyards, Jordan Vineyards, Stag's Leap Wine Cellars, Beaulieu Vineyards, Dunn Vineyards, Robert Mondavi Winery, Sterling Vineyards, Far Niente Winery, Silver Oak Cellars, Freemark Abbey, Conn Creek, Ridge Vineyards, Silverado Vineyards, Cosentino Reserve, Livington Vineyards, Beringer Vineyards and St. Clement Vineyards and DeLoach Vineyards.

ZINFANDEL

Zinfandel has always enjoyed a favorite-son status among Californians, perhaps because of the strong Italian influence in our state's history. While its ori-

147

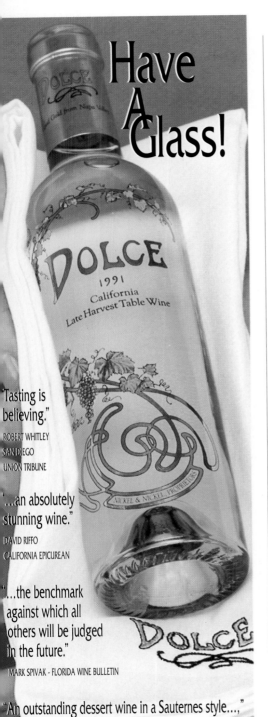

Have A Glass!

"Tasting is believing."

ROBERT WHITLEY
SAN DIEGO
UNION TRIBUNE

"...an absolutely stunning wine."

DAVID RIFFO
CALIFORNIA EPICUREAN

"...the benchmark against which all others will be judged in the future."

MARK SPIVAK - FLORIDA WINE BULLETIN

"An outstanding dessert wine in a Sauternes style...,"

THE WINE SPECTATOR

gins are definitely European, the grape is now grown mainly in California and is the most widely cultivated red wine grape. Winemakers value it for its versatility and adaptability. A medium-bodied, deeply colored red wine, Zinfandel tends toward the hearty style, but with an enticing blackberry flavor and a spicy personality, some of the preferred are: Ridge Vineyard, Fetzer Vineyards, Kendall Jackson Winery, Storybook Mountain Vineyards, Quivira Vineyards and Ravenswood.

MERITAGE

In the 1980s, many California Winemakers became intrigued by Bordeaux wines and began trying to replicate those famous clarets. By combining Cabernet Sauvignon with Merlot, Cabernet Franc and—when available—Malbec and Petit Verdot, winemakers created a type of wine unlike any one varietal. Before too long, an entirely new category of wine was created from traditional Bordeaux varieties and christened "Meritage," top-rated ones are: Opus One, M. Coz, Franciscan, Insignia, Merryvale and Cosentino Winery's The Poet.

DESSERT WINES

Dessert-style wines generally fall into two distinct types. The first includes wines labeled Late Harvest or something similar—most often made from Riesling or Semillon and, occasionally, from Sauvignon Blanc. Botrytis Cinerea, a naturally occuring mold, concentrates the grape sugars and imparts exotic fragrances and flavors. These wines depend on natural conditions and are not produced every year. The second type of dessert wine, typified by Sherry, Port and Madeira, is fortified by the addition of grapes spirits and produced every year.

"*You'll Find Dunnewood Chardonnay* THE CATCH OF THE DAY WITH MY SALMON AND LINGUINE."

Rozanne Gold, author of
Little Meals: A Great New Way to Eat & Cook.

"The subtle flavors of
Dunnewood Chardonnay
make it a perfect partner
for my Smoked Salmon with
Cucumber Linguine. Or most any fish
or poultry in a light cream or butter
sauce. I'm certain you'll love it.
In order to form a more perfect union,
bring Dunnewood to dinner."

IF ITS LEGENDARY IMAGE DOESN'T TEMPT YOU, SURELY THE RICHNESS OF ITS FLAVOR AND AROMA WILL

Experience this legendary "cigar of cigars" for yourself.
Some temptations are just too great to ignore.

BY RICHARD L. DI MEOLA

CIGAR SMOKING ENJOYS A RENAISSANCE

MARK TWAIN, A TRUE cigar lover, once said, "If I cannot smoke in heaven, I shall not go!"

Today, many people share the same opinion. Although it is certainly not a necessity, cigar smoking can be one of life's special pleasures. The aroma, ritual and draw, along with the feel of the cigar in one's mouth, comprise a total, satisfying experience.

Combined with an after-dinner libation, a fine cigar is the ultimate cap to a fine dinner. The smoker can sit back, relax and linger while the plates are cleared and the conversation mellows. Yet cigar lovers do not always wait for the evening meal to indulge in their passion. Many men enjoy a good smoke in the morning, perhaps an hour after breakfast. At this time of day, the cigar is no longer an extension of a repast. Instead it helps the smoker transcend his surroundings, giving him a moment to pause and reflect upon his activities and perhaps feel less hectic about them.

Lunch, too, is a favorite time for cigar smoking. The experience is different than the evening meal because it's generally without a complementary drink and the taste and aroma are a wonderful segue into the rest of the day. Usually light cigars are smoked by day, heavier ones at night.

Although there are no rules about when to smoke, there are often restrictions on where to smoke. More and more restaurants permit patrons to enjoy an after-dinner smoke, while others cater to the wishes of their non-smoking guests. Getting to know which restaurants are cigar friendly is one way to ensure a pleasant experience for all. Lately, though, interest in good cigars is enjoying a renaissance. Positive publicity about cigars has contributed to this, much of it from restaurants, hotels and clubs. All over America, these establishments have been conducting private smoker

dinners that sell out every time. From barbecue to black-tie, from $25 to $250 (there have been $1,000-a-plate charity smokers in New York and Paris), these affairs offer men, and women so inclined, the chance to gather over a meal and smoke cigars to their hearts' content.

About 1200 such events now take place a year. As a result, many fine restaurants have created separate, permanent smoking rooms and humidors are making a comeback. The main dining room is usually off-limits, but, more and more, smokers can adjourn to an adjoining lounge.

Not only that, but the $5 and $10 stogie is in great demand. It seems a more expensive cigar appeals to the psyche of some aficionados, just as an expensive watch appeals to its owner, yet there are some wonderful, inexpensive cigars available if the smoker does a little homework.

Typically, novices begin smoking cigars around the age of 30, They start as occasional smokers, for celebrations or during special events, and usually purchase more expensive cigars at the beginning. As the beauty and pleasure of smoking become apparent, they start indulging in a smoke alone. Next, they get to know a good tobacconist and explore the myriad of lower-priced cigars in the shop. Soon they are smoking cigars frequently and for less money.

Things get interesting when the smoker is more experienced. Exploring the multitude of blends, wrapper colors and sizes available and becoming conversant in cigars means the smoker is on the road to becoming an aficionado, a cigar lover who smokes six a week.

THE ORIGINS OF FINE CIGARS

The $10 cigars available in America today are most likely rolled in the Dominican Republic, Honduras, Jamaica or Mexico. There are others that come from the Canary Islands, Panama, Costa Rica and Nicaragua, but Dominican and Honduran cigars together make up 80% of the premium cigar market in the United States.

Cuban cigars are still illegal, but even before the Cuban embargo more than thirty years ago, cigars actually made in Cuba never accounted for more than 9% of the premium American market. That was when the most popular price category for the best cigars, Cuban or "Clear Havana," was 35 cents for a Corona shape, 42 ring by 5 1/2 inch length. (In America, a cigar's girth is measured by "ring" size, one ring being equivalent to 1/64th inch) Thus, the Corona is a bit more than 5/8 of an inch in diameter.

In the 1950s, more expensive, larger cigars sold for 65 to 70 cents. Clear Havana cigars were those made of 100% Havana tobacco, but rolled in the United States. All the best were made by hand, as the best Caribbean and Central American cigars are today. Thirty years ago, even lesser cigars contained some Havana tobacco because it was considered unparalleled in the world. In other words, in those days the important thing was not that cigars were rolled in Cuba, but that the tobacco was Cuban.

Now we have excellent tobacco growing in The Dominican Republic, Central America, Brazil, Cameroon, Mexico, Indonesia and other places. Former Cuban growers are no longer in Cuba today because they fled the country with their seeds which they planted, cultivated and nurtured in the countries mentioned above. There, they are now producing the finest, tastiest, most aromatic cigar tobaccos the world has ever known.

Sadly, the Cuban economy has slipped dramatically over the years, and fertilizers, insecticides and even expertise are scarce. As a result, the cigars being produced outside of Cuba today and regularly offered in the United States are the most superior. When Cuba finally rejoins the democratic community and the embargo is lifted, there will be renewed interest in Cuban cigars and tobacco. Cigar manufacturers will want to experiment with the blends they so painstakingly evolved over thirty years and bring new tastes, aromas and nuance to them by mixing in Cuban tobacco. But improving the current crop conditions in Cuba will take many years.

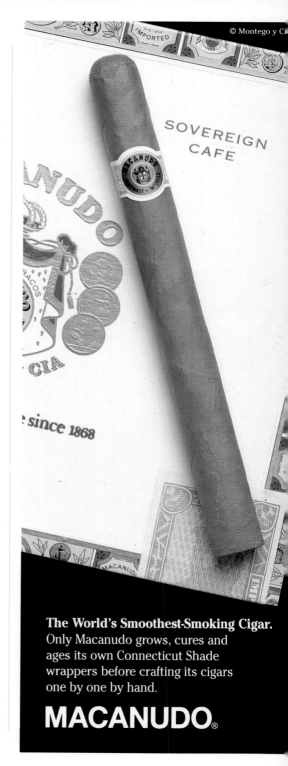

Los Libertadores
THE ULTIMATE CIGAR

**FOR MORE INFORMATION CALL
1-800-543-7131**

WRAPPERS

The tobacco used in brands available in America is the most expensive in the world. Wrapper tobacco, the half leaf wrapped around the outside of the cigar, the one the smoker sees and feels, is the most expensive, cultivated for eye appeal and smoothness to the touch. It is, after all, the part of the cigar that caresses its owner's lips.

One of the varieties most widely used is the Connecticut Shade Grown, grown in The Windsor Valley. It is allowed to sprout and mature under constructed layers of cheesecloth to protect it from the sun. The resulting leaf stays relatively light in color, although various shades of brown are yielded. The veins are acceptable, and the leaves are large and smooth. This tobacco presents the smoker with a perfect first impression. Lightness and smoothness portend mildness and a graceful taste. The best of this tobacco costs $40 per pound compared with many other types at $10 per pound.

Another popular wrapper is grown in Cameroon and Central Africa. This is Sun-Grown leaf, allowed to mature on the stalk without protection. It is a bit sandy and dark brown in color. Cameroon wrapper is sweeter and more aromatic than Connecticut Shade, but also thinner and more brittle.

Like food connoisseurs, most cigar aficionados "taste" with their eyes. While this is good, it is also important to enjoy the cigar for what it is, stripped of any visual cues.

Consider the Maduro wrapper. It is black and looks strong, even harsh. The best Maduro wrappers come from Mexico and Connecticut. Known as Connecticut Broadleaf, this Connecticut version is a heavy, veiny tobacco rich in oils, much like its Mexican relative. Dark to begin with, the tobacco when treated with heat and steam turns jet black. Before lighting up, one might think this cigar would be too harsh to enjoy, but this is not so. Properly treated, blended and rolled, Maduro wrapped cigars are often the sweetest and richest of all for those with an acquired taste.

Indonesian Java and Sumatra are good wrapper tobaccos that lend their own characteristics to the cigars they cover, as are the wrappers of Honduras, Ecuador and Nicaragua.

BINDERS AND FILLERS

The binder is another half leaf. It is rolled around the filler, forming what is called the "bunch." The binder's role is to hold the filler together so that the bunch can be presented to the wrapper for covering. It can affect the cigar's taste and aroma, so it must be carefully chosen, although the purpose of its heavy leaf is strength. The best binder in the world is Santo Domingo from the Dominican Republic. Mexican is a close second. Java third. If a manufacturer wants to add a nuance of taste and aroma, Java, Cameroon or even Connecticut might be used.

The filler in a fine, premium cigar is its soul. Never to be chopped up, as in inexpensive cigars, the leaves are folded into the cigar whole after being stripped of two-thirds of their center stems. In this condition, after preparation, they are called "frog strips," because the remainders of the leaves after stripping resemble dangling frogs legs. It is with these tobaccos that the cigar manufacturer can get creative and with them that growers have had success in cultivating magnificent strains of leaf.

The filler tobacco grown from Cuban seed in the Dominican Republic is called Piloto Cubano. It is rich, zesty and spicy tobacco. There are a couple of categories,"Seco" and "Ligero," and within each category, six to eight sub-types. Smart manufacturers know what each category and sub-type will bring to a blend and they experiment with them to create subtleties of taste and aroma.

There are also filler tobaccos grown from "home" seed in the Dominican Republic, Mexico, Java, Brazil, Honduras and other countries, each with their own unique characteristics. Deciphering the best ways to use these traits in blends takes years of experience. Even after a manufacturer has the knowledge, blending filler tobaccos, combining them with a binder and finishing the cigar with the proper wrapper is something like getting the tumblers of a lock to fall into place without

155

Ever Wonder What The Great Cuban Cigar Makers Did After Leaving Cuba?

Special Offer
We're getting so many compliments on our Dominican H. Upmann Cigars, we'll send you a sample of 12 Churchills, 5 1/2" x 46 ring, in a handsome gift box along with an H. Upmann Cigar Cutter and a copy of our 20 page booklet, "How to Judge A Good Cigar," all for $15.00 check or money order (retail value $35.00). Write: H. Upmann, P.O. Box 407166NA, Fort Lauderdale, FL 33340-7166. Allow (8) weeks for delivery. Offer expires December 31, 1995. Offer not available to minors. Limit one per customer.

knowing the combination. For the smoker, all the different brands and blends on the market make the task of finding what tastes best a similar mystique, but one that is fun, rewarding and indescribably pleasurable when discovered.

PUTTING IT ALL TOGETHER

Knowing the characteristics of tobaccos for blending is not enough. It is equally important to know how to roll. If the cigar is not properly constructed, it will not smoke well and the taste and aroma will be seriously flawed. The only way to make a fine cigar is by hand. No machine can "feel" the density of long filler along the length. The chopped up tobacco in short-filled cigars burns fast and hot, and such cigars do not hold their ash. Only those using frog-stripped filler leaves, folded together into their binders with skill, will burn slowly, evenly and cool.

Only a well-made cigar allows the blended leaf to deliver full richness of flavor. Flavor and aroma in cigars are described by those who make them with words like aromatic, sweet, zesty, peppery, piquant, pungent, floral, earthy, rich, full, light, grassy, woody and when the description isn't flattering, bitter, strong, harsh, astringent, dirty, acidic, ammoniacal.

The most frequent construction flaw in a cigar is hard draw. The most frustrating thing in the world for a cigar lover is to pay good money for a cigar and find that the smoke won't come out. Finding a knowledgeable tobacconist one can trust, preferably an avid cigar smoker, can help avoid this dilemma. Only after building up trust in the consistency of a cigar brand can the smoker label the brand a "good cigar."

The size of the cigar also makes a big difference in the delivery of taste and aroma. The 48 ring, 3/4 diameter has sufficient long filler to enable the manufacturer to be creative in his combinations. It also delivers a greater volume of smoke and richness. Thinner brands have fewer leaves in the blend and are therefore more simple, less complex. It is also more difficult to make the thinner brands by hand so the chance of getting one that doesn't burn properly is greater.

Cigar smokers usually experiment until they find the size suitable to their individual taste and then stick to it. If a smoker is looking for a favorite-sized cigar in a favorite brand and doesn't find it, chances are the smoker will select the same, tried-and-true size in another brand rather than make another size selection within the same brand.

When a great cigar is produced, it is crucial that it is kept in proper condition. A dry cigar will not be a good cigar, no matter how perfect it was when it left the manufacturer. It will smoke harsh and the wrapper is likely to unravel. Good merchants, therefore, religiously keep their stock in proper humidity. The smoker should, too. A humidor with a properly charged humidifier is the proper way to store cigars. The humidistat should always be pointed to "wet."

The enjoyment of fine cigars is a unique pleasure. It can be ritualistic or simple, whether the head of the cigar is opened with a gold cutter or the pinch of fingernails. The end that is lit, the tuck, is lit first before being placed in the mouth. Then the flame of a second match dances below the end of the cigar while drawing and twirling until the cigar is fully alight, ready to fulfill the smoker's expectation of spirited, spicy and aromatic richness.

There aren't any fast rules for smoking fine cigars other than considerate etiquette and common sense. Dining in restaurants where cigar smoking is welcomed doesn't mean ignoring nearby tables with guests in the middle of a meal. Adjourning to the lounge is still the right thing to do. On the other hand, in prohibitive restaurants, it is often possible to enjoy a cigar, after asking, when the establishment is not very full.

All cigar lovers should stay aware and practice smoking etiquette, and find the cigar of his, or her, dreams. ∎

Richard Di Meola *is the*
Executive Vice President, Chief Operating Officer of
Consolidated Cigar Corp. and a cigar lover.

JUAN CLEMENTE
"The Exceptional Cigar"

"The cigar made by an artisan for those who are epicurean connoisseurs, in love with fine food, good wines and tasty smoke."

RECOMMENDED TOBACCONISTS

Alfred Dunhill
Water Tower Place
835 North Michigan Avenue
Chicago, Illinois 60611
312-467-4455

Iwan Ries and Company
19 South Wabash Avenue 2nd Floor
Chicago, Illinois 60603-3010
800-621-1457

Jack Schwartz Importer
175 West Jackson Drive
Chicago, Illinois 60604
312-782-7898

Old Chicago Smoke Shop
10 South LaSalle Street
Chicago, Illinois 60601
312-236-9771

Rubovits Cigars
320 South LaSalle Street
Chicago, Illinois 60604
312-939-3780
800-782-8499

The Up Down Tobacco Shop
1550 North Wells Street
Chicago, Illinois 60610
312-337-8025
800-587-3696

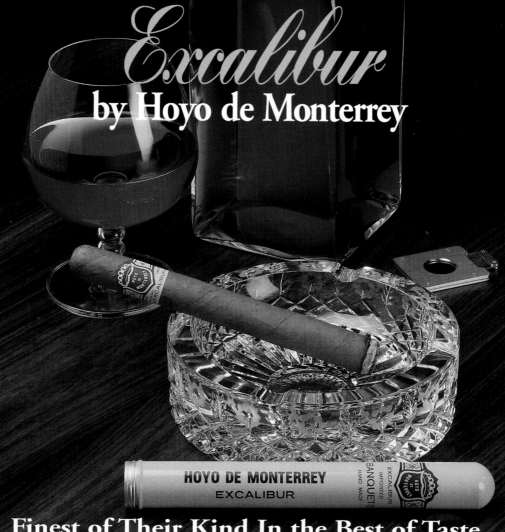

Davidoff

Call 1-800-328-4365 to inquire
about the restaurants, hotels,
resorts and clubs which have a
Davidoff or Zino Grande Reserve
Humidor or to order
The *Davidoff Cigar Smoker's
Guide to Restaurants*

Photograph by: Frank Navone

The Dominican Republic

The number one producer of premium cigars in the world.

BY MICHAEL FRANK

In the history of cigars the island nation of Cuba will always be a homeland and a promised land. From the dawn of industry to the Marxist Revolution and the rise of Fidel Castro, the tobacco business in Cuba was run by families whose first priority was quality. Their national heritage depended upon it. Indeed, mention the brands, "Partagas," "H.Upmann," or "Romeo y Julieta," and any elderly smoker who remembers those cigars in their prime will almost blush, dreaming of the smokes of yesteryear.

But today we cannot smoke history and dreams. The combined forces of weak production standards, social unrest, and a failure to properly finance the means of cigar production have undermined the quality of Cuban cigars. In the '90s, the epicure wants a consistently great cigar at a fair price, which is why, worldwide, the No. 1 producer of premium cigars is the Dominican Republic.

Produced on another island nation, those great brands from Cuba's past still exist, and in 1995 they are better than ever. The same Cuban families who made their names famous moved to the Dominican Republic and, 36 years after they produced the last Cuban cigars in their own Havana factories, make cigars with tobacco grown all over the globe.

Quality is not intangible. At the market or in the dining room, the gourmet knows a good cut of steak, a well-prepared pesto, or even an unadorned, dusty truffle. The best is simply better grown, better handled or better made. Cigars are no different. To excel you have to start with superior leaves. But only by adding them to the variables of well–trained labor, efficiency, and that nerve-racking intangible, self–conscious care, will you get great cigars. And the only place on the planet with a plentiful supply of all of these resources, and a stable economy, is the Dominican

Republic. First, the people are the warmest, gentlest and most conscientious anywhere, and many of them are independent farmers who depend on Dominican cigar manufacturers to buy their crops, so they have to care about their product. Then there's the soil, which is blessed by the forces of nature, combining near–perfect weather and mineral-balanced farmland in the Cibao river valley, near Santiago. And finally, there's the manufacturer whose cigars bear the touch of so many hands united in proud work, and a dedication to producing the best product.

Meet Your Producer

MATASA, or Manufactura de Tabacos S.A., is a great example of a successful family business, but more, the company's cigars are an excellent product. Despite small output (expected sales of 5.5 million hand-made cigars for 1995), Manuel Quesada's factory produces some of the most renowned cigars in the world. Each brand—Romeo y Julieta, Sosa, Fonseca, Licenciados, Casa Blanca, Cubita, Credo and José Benito—is successful because Manuel Quesada understands that his is a business of finite resources. With characteristic charm, Quesada explains that tobacco has it's own clock. If you're impatient with it, your cigars will suffer. "You cannot take leaves from a plant, roll them into cigars and smoke them, just as in wine you cannot take grapes, mash them and drink them. It depends on the plant variety—some take a year some take two years some take eight months, but they all take time."

Four generations of pride make MATASA a great manufacturer, but it's also the foresight to anticipate market demands that keeps Manuel Quesada's cigars exceptional in a universe of great Dominican product.

BENJAMIN F. MENENDEZ, (Benji, to his friends) bears the warm face and the firm handshake of a true gentleman. Born in Cuba, his family was responsible for the creation and production of the famous H. Upmann and Montecristo brands. But after the Revolution he and his family were forced to flee, first to Spain and the Canary Islands where a new family brand was created. Now, in the Dominican

Republic for more than a decade, Menendez is responsible for General Cigar's premium cigar production. He, along with several other "lifers" in the tobacco world, oversee one of the largest cigar operations in the world, with extensive buying power and the technical support capable of growing or sourcing enough tobacco to manufacture 17 million Dominican-produced, hand-made cigars in 1995.

MORE than any Dominican producer, the Arturo Fuente family has endured more than enough hardship just to make cigars. Since the 1920s they've set up shop in four different countries, including the United States. Only now, in a new promised land, are they thriving. The boom is back, and though they sweat it out, the Fuentes really do know the difference between labor just to pay the bills and the proud effort which results in a great product. Every cigar they make (and besides their own brands of Chateau de la Fuente, Arturo Fuente, Hemingway Series, and they also make Ashton, Cuesta-Rey, La Unica, Montesino and Bauza) is a testament to the belief in doing things just a little bit better... and then there's also the revolution. You see, the Fuente farm is more than a motivational tool created by some marketing whiz. It's a real farm, and today it is the symbol of a cigar nation rising to prominence, riding a revolutionary Dominican wave.

IF you're lucky enough to get to Casa de Campo in La Romana, the former playground of the Gulf & Western Corporation and presently one of the largest resorts in the Caribbean, you'll also be a golf-cart ride away from the Consolidated Cigar Corporation's Tabacalera de Garcia factory. It's not only located on a more beautiful site than the rest of the Republic's cigar factories, but it's also far more spacious, which has allowed Jose Seijas, vice president, general manager, to run the entire factory with greater efficiency than might be seen elsewhere. What does that mean to the smoker? Brands. Consolidated is responsible for more premium brands than any other producer on the island, from H. Upmann to Henry Clay, as well as Montecruz and even Dunhill. Another name to remember is Onyx 750. It is a great morning cigar.

HENDRIK KELNER is not a tobacco man in the most traditional sense—he's a man of science. If you really want to find out a little bit about tobacco, spend some time, perhaps a year or two, with Kelner. Only then will you begin to see a sliver of this man's knowledge. At his factory, Tabacos Dominicanos, familiarly known as

ONLY THE *BEST*...

Clockwise from lower right:
Carlos Fuente Jr.
Juan Clemente
Benjamin Menéndez
Guillermo León
Jose A. Seijas
Manuel Quesada
Modesto Garcia
Center:
Hendrik Kelner

PRODUCE THE *BEST* !

THE DOMINICAN REPUBLIC
CIGAR COUNTRY

Where quality is an art and tradition lives on...

TABADOM, Kelner's rollers make Avo, Troya, Griffins, PG , and in a separate facility, Davidoff. That last brand was the coup of a lifetime for Kelner, but it's also a huge responsibility. Zino Davidoff pulled his brand out of Cuba and rewarded it to Kelner's factory after quality concerns were not met, so it is obvious that at TABADOM, there can be no questions about workmanship. Davidoff re–inspects their cigars once they get to the U.S., so the cigars must be perfect. But then, other brands must also be perfect. If a complaint is made about any of the brands, Kelner is the first to know. Perfection is a daunting taskmaster, but not to a goal oriented man like Kelner.

IN any industry it's normal to have a maverick, even if it's only a matter of perception. In the cigar world, Jean Clemente, owner of Juan Clemente Cigars is a sort of rogue, a self-made man who went into the cigar business with no ties to tobacco, and no family history in the trade. He is an anomaly in a world usually reserved for custom and formality.

For 1995 Clemente's Santiago factory will produce a mere 600,000 cigars, with only two lines. Most manufacturers would get crushed in that kind of environment, but Clemente, a Frenchman by birth, doesn't appear to feel the affects of the competition, and his extreme patience with the process shows in the quality of his cigars, which are sold at a premium price and yet demand for them remains at an all–time high. Especially in Europe, where the market for the smallish, 5–inch by 30 ring–gauge cigars seems insatiable.

AS the eldest of four brothers, Don Eduardo Leon Jimenes is the patriarch of the oldest cigar manufacturer in the Dominican Republic. Since 1903, La Aurora S.A. has been selling cigars throughout Latin America, as well as to the local Dominican populace who couldn't afford Havanas. Now makers of two premium brands, Jimenes' father saw the company through some of the most trying times in his nation's history, and yet still managed to prosper.

Unique in the cigar world, La Aurora specifies a maximum allowable production quantity for each roller. This kind of strategy and care has paid off for the past 92 years. There's little doubt they'll be there 92 years from now. ■

Michael Frank *is the former*
Assistant Editor of **Cigar Aficionado** *magazine.*

He Created The Most Accommodating Tavern In America.

Warner LeRoy, Owner, Tavern On The Green

It's more "theatre in the park" than tavern. A whimsical stage created by a consummate showman with the instinct to know that great accommodations are more than just great food. In the magical environs of this tavern, there is something for everyone. But Warner LeRoy's theatrical style isn't all that makes Manhattan's Tavern On The Green the top-grossing restaurant in America. It's his talent for making visitors from anywhere on the globe feel welcome. Which is why the Tavern displays this sign. It means whether you smoke or not, you'll be accommodated.

The Sign Of An Accommodating Restaurant.

**NON-SMOKERS
AND SMOKERS
WELCOME**

Sponsored by The Accommodation Program, New York, NY

RESTAURANT INDEX

SAN FRANCISCO

Acquerello • ITA 17
Alain Rondelli • FRN 18
Alfred's Steakhouse • STK 19
Anjou • FRN 20
Aqua • SEA 16
The Big Four • CON 24
Bistro M • CAL/FRN 23
Bix • AMR 25
Boulevard • AMR 26
Brasserie Savoy • FRN/AMR..................29
Buca Giovanni • ITA 30
Carnelian Room • AMR 31
Cypress Club • AMR 32
Ernie's • FRN 33
Fleur de Lys • FRN 34
Fly Trap • SFR 37
Fog City Diner • AMR 38
Harris' • STK 39
House of Prime Rib • STK 40
Imperial Palace • CHI 42
Kuleto's • ITA 43
La Brasserie Française • FRN 44
La Folie • FRN 45
La Pergola • ITA 46
Le Central • FRN 48
Le Club • MED 49
L'Olivier • FRN 50
MacArthur Park • AMR 54
The Mandarin • CHI 55
Masa's • FRN 53
McCormick & Kuleto's • SEA 56
Moose's • AMR 57
Morton's of Chicago • STK 58
One Market • AMR 60
Oritalia • ORI/ITA 61
Pacific • CAL 62
Palio d'Asti • ITA 63
Park Grill • AMR 66
Postrio • AMR 64
Prego • ITA 67
Rôti • AMR 68
Rubicon • COM FRN 69
Silks • CAL 73
Splendido • MED 72
Stars • AMR 70
Tommys Toy's • CHI 74
Venticello • ITA 75
Vertigo • COM 76
Victor's • CAL/FRN 77

MARIN COUNTY

Buckeye Roadhouse • AMR 80
Joe LoCoco's • ITA.........................81
The Lark Creek Inn • AMR 82
Mikayla at Casa Madrona • AMR 83
Savannah Grill • AMR 84
Tutto Mare • ITA/SEA 85

EAST BAY

Bay Wolf • MED 87
Blackhawk Grille • CAL 88
Chez Panisse • MED 90
Lalime's • MED 89
Maximillian's • CON 92
Oliveto • ITA 93
Rivoli • AMR 94
Tourelle • MED 95

SOUTH BAY

Birk's • AMR 98
California Cafe Bar & Grill • CAL 99
Chef Chu's • CHI 100
Emile's • FRN 101
Fisherman Bar & Grill • ITA/SEA 102
Flower Lounge • CHI 105
Le Mouton Noir • FRN 106
Le Papillon • FRN 107
Paolo's Restaurant • ITA 108
231 Ellsworth • FRN 109

WINE COUNTRY

Auberge du Soleil • CAL 112
Brava Terrace • CAL 114
Cafe Lolo • CAL 115
Domaine Chandon • FRN 116
East Side Oyster Bar & Grill • CAL 117
French Laundry • AMR/FRN 118
John Ash & Co. • CAL 119
Mixx • WIN 120
Mustards Grill • CAL 122
Napa Valley Grille • WIN 123
Piatti (Yountville) • ITA 124
The Restaurant at Meadowood • FRN 125
Showley's • CAL 126
Terra • CAL 127
Tra Vigne • ITA 128

MONTEREY/CARMEL

Anton & Michel • CON 131
The Avenue • AMR..........................132
Covey • EUR 133
The French Poodle • FRN 134
The Grill on Ocean Avenue • CAL/ASN 135
Melac's • FRN 136
The Terrace Grill • CAL/INT 137

YOSEMITE

Erna's Elderberry House • FRN 138

CUISINE KEY

AMR =	American	ITA =	Italian
ASN =	Asian	MED =	Mediterranean
CAL =	California	MEX =	Mexican
CHI =	Chinese	ORI =	Oriental
COM =	Contemporary	SFR =	San Francisco
CON =	Continental	SEA =	Seafood
EUR =	European	SWS =	Southwest
FRN =	French	STK =	Steakhouse
INT =	International	WIN =	Wine Country